Great Galloping Catfish!

To St. Michael's School:
Enjoy!

John Darling
2008

Saint Michael School
1204 11th Ave SE
Olympia, WA 98501

Great Galloping Catfish!

(and other slightly improbable stories)

being an account of a year or so spent
at Ruination Farm and some strange
adventures which befell and otherwise
happened to me there

by Grandpappy
(as told to John Dashney)

WW

Wicklewood Books

Wicklewood Books
1932 Chemeketa
Salem, OR 97301

(Wicklewood Books is an imprint of The Stage Within Your Mind)

First Edition, First Printing

ISBN:0-9633236-5-2

Library of Congress Control Number:
                                2004102975

Layout and design by DIMI PRESS

Cover art and illustrations by Sheila Somerville

To the memory of

Baron Karl Von Munchausen

(1720-1797)

Grandpappy's fourth cousin
A few times removed
(and we won't say where)
on the distaff side

Truth is like salt.
You need a pinch or two
To give your story added flavor and zest.
But don't put in too much
Or your audience will make a face
And spit it out.

—Grandpappy

The Flying Snake

I.

Oh Johnny! Did I ever tell you about the time I taught a snake to fly? Well, it's not an easy thing to do, let me assure you. But I managed it, and old Arnold Bennett became a first-rate, class-A pilot. Let me tell you how it all happened.

I suppose it all started with those dadburn crows that were raiding my corn patch down along the river. You know that my stretch of bottomland along the Windy River is about the best kind of soil there is for growing anything you could name, and I was fixing that year to raise me a crop of popping corn that would put old Orville Whatshisname to shame. But those blasted crows seemed bound and determined to thwart me.

They'd roost in the trees over on the far side of the river, and then right at first light, just as the sun was poking up over the top of the Dismal Hills, they'd swoop across and hit that corn patch just like that Plague of Locusts mentioned somewhere in the Bible. I'd run out and shoo 'em off, but they'd just fly back across the river and wait for me to go about

1

my business elsewhere. Then back they'd come again.

It was easy enough to spot their leader. He was a big old white crow. I could sense right away that he was the one that was full of Old Nick. The others just seemed to follow his lead and do what he told 'em to.

Now why that old white rascal had it in for me and my corn patch—well, I wouldn't have the faintest notion. But he sure did, and I was developing a bad case of the blue jimhickies fretting over how I could stop him. You talk about things being black with sin? Well, this particular critter was *white* with sin, and I guess that makes matters even worse.

Johnny, I was afraid I'd have to break a vow I had made never to kill another one of the Good Lord's critters. In fact, I was just making plans to head into town and buy me a shotgun and a box of number four shells when it happened.

I noticed a commotion down by the barn, and when I investigated, I saw it was that old white crow and two or three of his followers. They were hopping around on the ground and pecking at something. I couldn't tell from a distance just what it was, but if those crows were interested in it, then I thought I'd better investigate.

Turned out it was a snake. A king snake, as a matter of fact. The scientific folks give the genus a real fancy name—*lampropeltis*. But to me they're just king snakes. Unfortunately, this particular specimen wasn't king-size yet, and that was his problem.

He was just a little too small to defend himself against those pestiferous crows. Maybe he could have held his own against one of them, but not against three or four. They were taking turns hopping in or swooping down, taking a peck or two at him and then dodging away before he could strike back. Of course you know that king snakes aren't poisonous. So even if this little fellow had connected, he couldn't have done very much damage.

Now I like having king snakes around Ruination Farm. They keep the bugs down, and once in a while they might catch a mouse—which are critters I *don't* particularly like to have around. Besides, those crows really didn't need to kill that snake. There was plenty of food for them elsewhere. They were pecking at him just to be mean—just because they held the advantage, and there really wasn't anything he could do about it.

So I shooed them off, and there I was with an injured king snake on my hands. Well, I'd saved him, so he was my responsibility. I picked him up as carefully as I could and carried him into the house. He seemed so sense that I meant him no harm, and thus offered no objections—not that he could have done much even if he'd wanted to. Those marauderous crows had come pretty darn close to finishing him off.

What's that, Johnny? *Marauderous?* I made it up. It's a combination of *marauding* and *murderous*, and I think it describes those pesky critters pretty well.

I'd studied a little about animal doctoring back in my earlier days. Not very much about fixing up snakes, mind you, but I speculated that what was good for one critter was probably good for another. So I cleaned and bandaged his wounds as best I could and put him in a box I'd lined with some old rags.

"Sorry it's not a fancier place," I said to the snake, "but it's the best I can do on short notice. I'll see if I can rustle you up something to eat. A little grub always tends to speed up the healing process."

Of course, I wasn't expecting any answer. So you can just imagine my surprise when a teeny tiny voice said, "Thank you very much."

"Great galloping catfish!" I cried. "Did you just say something?"

And that little teeny tiny voice said, "Yes, I said thank you very much."

"You mean to tell me you can talk?"

"Just a little," the snake replied. "I haven't had much practice."

"And why is that?" I wondered.

"Well, ever since my ancestor way, way back in the Bible had that conversation with Eve in the Garden of Eden, things have gone downhill for us. We're taught from the time we first hatch that it's just not a good idea to let humans know we can talk. I only spoke because you were so kind and I wanted to thank you. But please don't let any other snakes know about this. I could get in a lot of trouble."

"All right, I won't," I agreed. "I don't make a habit of talking to snakes anyway. But what about that offer of a little something to eat?"

"It sure sounds pretty good," the snake said.

"What would you fancy? I'm afraid I don't know all that much about your diet."

"I don't want to put you to any trouble, but if you could turn over a rock or an old board and bring me two or three of those white grubs you find under them, I'd be much obliged." He paused in thought for a moment, then added, "Of course, if you happened to find a nice fat earthworm, that would be even better."

"I'll see what I can do," I told him.

"Well, well, well!" I said to myself as I started out the door. "If this ain't enough to roast the rutabaga!" (I would have said it was a pretty kettle of fish, except I didn't have a kettle and I wasn't after fish.) I was heading out with an old tuna can that I'd scrounged from the recycling box to hunt up some grubs and a worm or two to serve as dinner for an injured talking snake. I guess it's a good example of the strange things that sometime happen out at Ruination Farm.

But it was only a few minutes' work rounding up dinner for the little critter. I could have filled the entire can easily, but I only took a few grubs and a couple of worms. You don't want to overfeed an invalid. It's bad for the system. However, the snake seemed happy with what I brought him.

"Just right!" the little critter said after he'd polished off the last grub. "Best dinner I've had in ages. Thank you ever so kindly, Sir. I'm almost embarrassed to ask you for another favor, but may I?"

"I suppose so. What is it?"

Could you put my box in a nice cool corner during the heat of the day and then move it over by the wood stove if it gets real cold tonight? I'm afraid I'm not warm-blooded like you are."

"Won't be any trouble at all," I said and moved his bed over to a dark corner by the bookshelf, where the snake curled up and promptly went to sleep.

II.

Johnny, you might be wondering just how this particular king snake came to have the name of Arnold Bennett, since it sure wasn't the name he came into the world with. As a matter of fact, he didn't have any name at all. Apparently snakes don't bother with them.

I remember that on the following day I asked him just what he was called, and this funny kind of shaky motion rippled down his entire length. It looked like he was trying to shrug his shoulders, but of course he didn't have any.

"I don't believe I have a name," he said. "How do I go about getting one?"

"Well," I replied, "with us humans, it's the parents who give you the name as soon as you're born. In fact, they give you two or three of them."

"Could you give me one then?" he asked.

"I suppose I could. How about a full set? It wouldn't be any extra trouble."

"That would be nice," the snake agreed.

"Let's see then. The biology fellows put you in the genus *lampropeltis*, so that can be your last name. Now the first and middle names should be more significant, something that really sets you apart from the crowd."

All the while I was telling him this, my gaze was wandering around the room seeking some kind of inspiration. Finally my eyes lighted on a book lying on the table beside my reading chair. The title of this particular volume was *The Old Wives Tale*, and

the author's name (as you should know) was Arnold Bennett. So I made the snake an offer.

"How about Arnold Bennett Lampropeltis? The first two belong to the fellow that wrote this book, but he's been dead for years and years. So I don't think he would mind if we borrowed his name."

"Ar-nold Ben-nett Lam-pro-pel-tis!" The snake said it very slowly, letting the syllables roll off his little forked tongue. "I like that! It has a kind of...of..."

"A kind of ring to it?" I suggested, and the snake nodded in agreement.

"Yes! It makes me feel inportant and significant—like I really count for something! By the way, what should I call you?"

"Most folks around here just call me Grandpappy," I said.

"*Just* Grandpappy? Nothing more than that?"

"Oh, I have some other names, but Grandpappy is the one I like best."

"Then that's what I will call you," said the snake. "Grandpappy, do you suppose you could hunt me up a few more grubs and maybe a worm or two? Getting a name has made me kinda hungry again."

III.

Meanwhile, all was not well out at Ruination Farm. I'd given my place that name after all my friends had said, when I announced my plans to move here, "Grandpappy, that place will be your ruination for sure!" Now I will admit that I'm clear out six miles north of Nowhere, but I like it. The air is clear, the pace is slow and life is generally peaceful—but just then it wasn't. I had two ponderous and perplexing problems that I was going to have to deal with.

The first, of course, concerned those marauderous crows. Thanks to them I now had an invalid king snake to care for, and that was my second problem. Until he had recovered enough to go back outdoors, Arnold Bennett would have to share my house with Hairball, my totally dysfunctional and paranoid cat.

That poor old feline believed that all the mice in the world were united in a conspiracy against him—that if he went outside for more than a few minutes, he would be seized by a posse of six thousand mice, brought before a mouse tribunal and charged with crimes against mousedom. Then he would be nibbled to death by hundreds of vengeful relatives of his former victims. Such fears do not make for a healthy mind.

Unfortunately, Hairball's paranoia did not extend to snakes—especially not to smaller, injured snakes who did not look like they could put up much of a fight. No, I'm afraid this aroused that cat's baser instincts, and I had to lecture him sharply, threaten him with being put out in the great outdoors and even reach for the rubfurong which I kept on a hook over the fireplace before he would agree to leave poor Arnold Bennett alone.

What's a *rubfurong*, you ask? It's a little device I invented for disciplinary measures when psychology and counseling failed to work on that cat. It doesn't actually hurt him—I'd never do anything to harm the worthless old rascal. But just one swipe puts every hair on his useless old carcass clean out of place, and you know how a cat hates to have its fur rubbed the wrong way. It takes him more than an hour to get everything back in place, and by then he's had a chance to calm down and think things through.

But while I was putting my household in order, those crows had not been idle. When I went out with the tuna can to collect a few more grubs, I saw them down in the corn patch having their fun at my expense. I'd put up a scarecrow, but that old white devil just perched himself right on its head to direct operations. Then he deliberately turned his back to me, raised his tail feathers and made a mess right on that poor scarecrow's face!

I yelled, tossed a few rocks their way and then stomped back into the house with the tuna can empty. I must admit I was not in the best of moods just then.

"Why, what's the matter, Grandpappy?" Arnold Bennett sounded a little more disappointed than concerned. I guess he could see that the tuna can was empty.

"Come on outside with me and I'll show you!" I said as I picked him up and set him carefully in my jacket pocket. I took him out and pointed to the crows that were circling out over the river, just beyond rock range.

"*That's* what's the matter!" I said. "What am I ever going to do with those dang-blasted marauderous crows? I hate to think on it, but I'm afraid I'm going to have to get myself a shotgun and shoot a few of 'em out of the sky."

Now I wasn't sure just how the snake would react to that. Considering what they had done to him, he might be all for it. Or he might be dead against it, having a rather sensitive soul (for a snake, that is). But Arnold Bennett just looked up at those circling crows and sighed.

"Just think what it must feel like, Grandpappy! Riding on the wind high over the earth and looking down upon us poor creatures chained to the ground!" I could swear that snake had a streak of poetry in his makeup.

"Yeah, it must really be something," I admitted.

"Have you ever flown, Grandpappy?"

"Well, never under my own power, but I've gone up in an airplane a few times."

"What's an airplane?" the snake asked.

"It's a contraption we humans use for getting ourselves up in the air," I told him.

The snake looked at me in kind of a funny way and said, "Tell me more."

So I did, and as I explained the basic principles of aircraft design, a thought began forming itself in my head. *Why not use a model airplane against those crows?* Sure! Why not? I could run 'em right out of the corn patch, chase 'em clear across the Windy River and maybe even have a little fun in the process.

"I'd give anything to be able to fly!" Arnold Bennett said as he watched the crows circling and swooping over the river.

It is indeed a wonderful thing when two problems come together and create their own solution. I needed a way to deal with those marauderous crows, and Arnold Bennett wanted to experience flight. A model airplane looked like the answer for both of us.

"Maybe there is a way," I said to the snake. "I'll drive into town tomorrow and see if I can't find something that will work for both of us."

IV.

I don't go to town very often, living six miles north of Nowhere as I do—plus I'd have to go a ways beyond Nowhere to find the supplies I needed. But I made the trip, as much for Arnold Bennett's sake as for my own.

I found a store that carried hobby supplies and model airplanes. I needed something with an open cockpit big enough for a small king snake to fit himself into. That eliminated all the modern-day models and took me clear back to the era of World War I fighters. I looked at a bunch of them before finally choosing a German Fokker D-7. That's not the kind the Red Baron flew, but he probably would have if he'd lived a mite longer.

I took the kit home with me and started assembling it that very night. It had a nice little engine and a remote-control panel that I could hold and control its flight from the ground. It was just the proper size to hold that snake nice and snug, and everything was done to scale. The only things that didn't work were the guns. They were dummies, and that was fine with me. The idea of a snake flying around the sky in a fighter armed with two real machine guns was not all that appealing.

"Arnold," I said as the snake watched me put the finishing touches to the model, "are you abso-positively certain you want to go up in this?"

"Grandpappy, I've never been surer of anything in all my life!" he replied.

"Then I guess I'd better add a little seat belt to hold you in, just in case I happen to send it into a loop. Then, come tomorrow at first light, I'll send you up!"

Well, I don't think that snake slept a wink that night. He crawled right up onto my pillow just before dawn and hissed in my ear, "Grandpappy! Grandpappy! Wake up! Daylight will be here in just a few minutes!"

So I crawled out of bed and got myself dressed. That snake thought it was highly amusing that I put on different clothes every morning. He only changed his skin once a year, he informed me. Then we went out to the barn and I gassed up the plane.

"Let me try it once without you," I told him. "I want to make sure I can do things right and proper." I started the engine, sent it up, and the plane performed just like the instruction manual said it would. When I brought it back in for a landing, old Arnold was so doggone eager that he nearly slithered right into the prop before I could cut off the engine.

"Keep your skin on!" I warned him. "You snakes have been waiting several million years to get up in the air. A few more minutes isn't going to hurt you."

I set that snake in the cockpit and fastened the seat belt as snug as I could. Then I started the engine, pointed the plane's nose into the wind and sent it up in the air. I thought I'd take it real easy the first time or two, since I wasn't sure if snakes got airsick or not. But then I saw the crows and forgot all about caution.

There were two of them, out over the river and coming our way for an early-morning look-around—or reconnaissance—I guess that's the proper military term. Anyhow, they saw this strange-looking contraption flying over the corn patch and thought they'd take a closer look at it. I couldn't resist the temtation. I spun that Fokker D-7 around in a tight turn and sent it straight at them!

When that pair of crows saw that model fighter plane coming at them—well, they just about had a pair of heart attacks right there on the spot! They flipped around and high-tailfeathered it back across the river, cawing and squawking like one of those great galloping catfish had suddenly sprouted wings and was trying to grab them for its breakfast. From the way they carried on, that may have been just what they thought.

I let Arnold Bennett have the fun of chasing them about halfway back before I pulled him up, turned him around in an Immelmann Roll and brought him back to my side of the river. I didn't want to let him stray beyond the range of my remote. That would have been bad for the both of us.

When the D-7 landed and I cut the engine, I expected that poor snake would be half dead and nine-tenths sick with fear. An Immelmann, after all, is a half-loop followed by a half-roll that brings you out flying in the opposite direction at full speed. It's not meant for the faint of heart or queasy of stomach. But

Arnold slithered out of the cockpit with a look of pure radiance on his reptilian face.

"Oh Grandpappy!" he hissed. "What we've been missing all these years! If only my ancestor had kept his big mouth shut back there in the Garden! When I think of all the snakes who've gone before me and never had the chance..." And would you believe it? He actually began to cry.

"I take it you enjoyed the experience then?" I asked.

"Enjoyed it! It was the most wonderful, thrilling, exciting, gorgeous, beautiful, marvelous..." He paused at this point to wipe his eyes with the tip of his tail and try to think of a few more adjectives.

"You don't have to say any more," I told him. "I get the picture."

V.

Well, from that moment on Arnold Bennett Lampropeltis was a snake possessed by the love of flight. Every day, early in the morning and late in the afternoon, I had to take him out by the corn patch, strap him into that plane and fly him out over the Windy River. Then I'd bring him back over land again and put him through a series of loops, spins, turns, twists and dives until I would get a little queasy just from watching. But that snake wasn't bothered a bit. The only thing to irritate him was when I cut the engine and brought him back to earth.

"Aw, Grandpappy!" he'd complain. "Couldn't I stay up just a little longer?"

"Look here!" I'd say. "As it happens, I have other things to do. There's a bit more to running a farm than giving flying lessons to a snake."

So, right after landing one morning, Arnold Bennett came up with an idea.

"Suppose you were to rig up this plane so I could fly it myself. Wouldn't that be better for both of us? You wouldn't have to waste your time at the controls, and I could practice by myself."

Now I'll admit the idea had some merit, though I had some misgivings about turning a snake loose in the sky. I did like the challenge, though. Would it be possible to rig the controls so that Arnold Bennett could fly solo? Well, there was just one way to find out.

Real World War I pilots had a control stick they worked with their hands and a rudder bar they controlled with their feet—so you could say that Arnold Bennett was at a bit of a disadvantage, since he had none of the above. I was going to have to develop a set of controls he could operate with his tail. It took about a week's worth of ingenuity, but I finally came up with a set that I thought—I hoped—I prayed—might work. I showed Arnold the results and asked if he was game enough to have a try.

Well, I have to say that snake was pure sand and grit straight through to his reptilian backbone. I set him in the cockpit that night and had him work the controls with his tail until it looked like he had the hang of it. But I was still worried. It's one thing to sit safely on the ground and play with the controls. But to do it two hundred feet up, where a single mistake could mean a crash—that's another matter altogether.

But the very next morning, just before daylight, Arnold Bennett was up on my pillow and hissing in my ear that he was ready and could we please get started right away? I insisted on making a pot of coffee first and asked him if he wanted any, but he shook his scaly head. Just the thought of flying solo had him wired enough already.

By the time I'd fetched the plane from the barn, checked the fuel to make sure he had enough and strapped him into the pilot's seat, the sun was poking up over the top of the Dismal Hills to the east. I'd prepared a little runway out by the corn patch where he could take off and land without too many bumps—provided he knew what he was doing. But the only way to learn was though experience, and the only way to get experience was to fly. So I used the remote to start the engine, pointed the Fokker's nose into the wind and told him he was cleared for takeoff.

Oh Johnny! That plane roared straight down the runway and rose into the air with nary a bump and scarcely a lurch. "A natural pilot!" I marveled as he circled once or twice to gain altitude. But then he headed right out over the Windy River.

"Hold on! Not that way!" I shouted. I'd warned him about the river the night before. If he came down in the water, he just might be able to undo the strap and get free before the plane sank, but he still faced a mighty tough swim back to shore—and those great galloping catfish that lived along the bottom? They could sense when someone on the surface was in trouble, and if that someone was the size of poor Arnold, they'd probably consider it an invitation to a free breakfast and be on him in less time than it takes me to tell you about it.

Then I saw what had caught that snake's attention. A single crow came flying out over the river, heading our way and taking his time about it. He reminded me a bit of an old World War I observation plane out to photograph enemy positions. Well, that observation crow had an enemy fighter bearing down on him, as he soon discovered.

Arnold Bennett flew straight at him, and that poor crow was almost too shocked to dodge. Almost, but not quite. He ducked under the Fokker at the last possible instant. Through my binoculars I saw the propeller blades just clip the ends of his tail feathers. Both plane and crow gave a lurch, and the crow fluttered back to the trees kind of wobbly-like, while Arnold Bennett brought his plane around in a Lufbury Circle and headed back to the airstrip.

"Did you see that, Grandpappy?" he hissed as he released the belt and slithered out of the cockpit. "Wasn't it incredible? Wasn't it fantastic?"

"I think it's one of the most dang-fool stupid stunts it has ever been my misfortune to witness! Do you realize just how close you came to getting yourself killed?"

"Do *you* realize just how close I came to knocking that crow right out of the sky?" Apparently that snake wasn't a bit fazed by my anger. "Did he make it back to the trees?"

"Yes, just barely," I said. I was still mad, but I had to concede that old Arnold had made a pretty slick job of it.

"Grandpappy! Do you realize I just made history? For the first time in the whole history of the world, a snake has fought and defeated a bird *in the bird's own element!* It's never happened before!"

"And it's not likely to happen again, if you're going to be that dang careless," I told him. "Your job is to protect my corn patch, not fight a one-snake war against every critter that can fly. If you'd hit that crow squarely, you'd have brought him down, all right. But you'd have gone down with him—right into the river! And those great galloping catfish would have had the both of you for breakfast!

Arnold hung his reptilian head for a moment and then said, "I guess you're right, Grandpappy. I kinda got carried away." But then he grinned a snaky grin and added, "I think it would have been worth it, though, just to know I had won."

"No it wouldn't!" I insisted. "Not to me! That's a valuable airplane. I don't get them for free, after all. And you count for something too," I added with a smile.

Arnold Bennett looked kind of surprised and pleased all at once. "Do you really think so?" he asked me. "No one's ever told me that before."

"Well, you do count for something. But if you're going to mix it up with those murauderous crows, then I'd better teach you something about basic tactics." (You see, Johnny, I did a bit of stunt flying back in my younger days—though modesty compels me to add that I never was a wartime combat pilot.)

"What's tactics?" Arnold Bennett wanted to know.

"How to take advantage of your strengths and minimize your weaknesses," I explained. "Look here now. You're faster than those crows, but they can outmaneuver you. So what you need to do is get above 'em and then dive right through their formation and make 'em scatter. Don't try to get in a circling match with 'em. They can turn a tighter circle than *you* can."

"Is that what the humans who fly the big planes do?"

"Sometimes. Back in the days when planes like this were used as weapons, the idea was to get behind your opponent and use the guns to shoot him down. They'd never try to ram unless they were eager to commit suicide."

Arnold Bennett stared wistfully at the dummy guns mounted on that Fokker D-7. Then he gave me his best reptilian smile and said, "Grandpappy, you don't suppose…"

"No I don't!" I replied before he could finish. "They don't make guns that small, and even if they did, I wouldn't arm that plane!" Just the thought of a snake prowling the sky with loaded guns was enough to scare the blue jimhickies out of me.

"But then how am I going to knock any of them down?"

"You're not! All I need you to do is scare the blue jimhickies out of *them* and keep 'em on the far side of the river. If I really wanted to do mortal damage, I would have bought myself a shotgun instead of this plane."

"Well, I can sure scare them for you, Grandpappy. That engine is loud enough to terrorize just about any creature that slithers, walks or flies."

That reminded me of another question I had meant to ask that snake. "Look here now," I said to him. "I read somewhere that snakes are supoosed to be deaf. How come you hear me so well?"

Arnold Bennett gave me that sidelong, guilty look that children will sometimes give their parents when Mom or Dad has caught them doing something they shouldn't. "Don't let on I told you this, but that's what we *want* folks to think," he confided. "You can learn a lot and avoid considerable trouble by pretending not to hear. *'Sometimes it's better to keep quiet and be thought a fool than...'*

'...than to speak up and remove all doubt,' I concluded. I was beginning to see that the mind of a snake ran a lot deeper than I first thought.

VI.

For the next three days Arnold Bennett ruled the sky—or at least the sky over my corn patch. The crows would come over two to three times a day. But as soon as they saw that snake take off, they'd hightailfeather it back to the trees on the far side. Arnold took to strutting around the corn patch like it was his own little kingdom. You may think it impossible for a snake to strut, but

Arnold did. It was kind of a slither-strut, in fact. Arnold seemed to think he was invincible, but I had a few doubts and worries.

Chief among these was that sneaky white crow. I never saw him in anypatrols that flew across the river, but I spotted him a couple of times through my binoculars. He'd be flying lazy circles above the trees on the far side, apparently keeping an eye on things while he plotted some new kind of deviltry. Arnold Bennett would soon get a taste of it.

On the fourth morning a group of five or six crows took off right at first light, circled above the trees for a few minutes and then headed our way. Arnold's plane was gassed up and ready to go, and I'd moved his little bed out to the corn patch so he could take off at a moment's notice. He was in the cockpit before I had the engine started and the plane turned into the wind for takeoff. The Fokker D-7 roared down the runway, rose into the air and set off to intercept them.

Then I saw what that old white devil had been up to.

That formation of crows broke apart when Arnold Bennett dived on them, but they regrouped as soon as he had passed through. The snake pulled up in an Immelmann Roll and went at them again, but he forgot to watch his own tail. And it was then that the old white crow sprang his trap.

A second formation, led by that old white rascal himself, flashed down from out of the sun, and Arnold suddenly found himself surrounded. Crows zoomed down on him from above and up at him from below. He had crows in front and crows on either side, and I could see they meant to hem him in and force him down.

None of them were foolish enough to crash into him head on, but that old white imp had figured correctly that the Fokker's wings and tail were vulnerable. So that's what they went for.

"Arnold!" I cried. "Break it off and get back here! You can't fight the whole bunch!"

The idea suddenly seemed to have great appeal for Arnold too, but getting back was going to be a bit more difficult than he had figured. The crows had him blanketed from above, and the ones in front and on the sides hemmed him in so that he couldn't use the plane's superior speed to break clear. Yes, Johnny, things looked pretty bleak for Arnold Bennett Lampropeltis—and for a plane that had set me back a good deal of money.

I guess that snake figured he was done for. But if he was going down, he apparently decided to take one of those blasted birds with him. He suddenly gave his plane full throttle and aimed straight for a crow in front of and just a little below him. I saw feathers and bits of feathers fly and heard one terrible squawk. Then that poor crow dropped right into the river like a piece of black rock!

That poor crow didn't even have time to drown. I saw a bubbly commotion in the water beside the bird as a great galloping catfish rose up from the bottom, clamped its jaws onto the crow and vanished again quicker than I could say, "Well, I declare!" Arnold Bennett had brought down his first crow!

But it appeared he was going in himself. The collision had stopped his engine cold. He pointed his plane for the bank, but I could tell right off that he didn't have the height nor the speed to make it back. It was sure lucky for him that I had my rescue kit ready to hand!

Johnny, did I ever mention that I was the Snodgrass County All-Around Fly-Casting Champion eleven years running? Well, I was—though modesty compels me to add that I did lose a couple of times when I was young and inexperienced.

But I had brought along my best rod, some ten-pound test line and a big old barbed hook for just such an emergency. I flipped out that line, snagged that plane on its upper wing when it wasn't more than a couple of feet above the river and began reeling it in as fast as I could!

I had that D-7 within ten feet of the shore when its wheels touched water and it began to settle. But I pulled extra hard and got Arnold Bennett out onto the gravel of the riverbank just as I saw another bubbly commotion in the water behind him. Another great galloping catfish came flopping right onto the shore in hot pursuit. Those catfish sure don't give up easily!

But I dropped the rod and grabbed up the other half of my rescue kit—a golf club—and I gave that catfish a lick that made it yelp and tumble back into the river. (What's that, Johnny? You don't think a catfish can yelp? Well, whack him one on the snout with a seven-iron and he'll yelp, all right!)

Arnold Bennett slithered out of the cockpit, gave me a snaky smile and said, "I did it, Grandpappy! I bagged my first crow! Did you see him go down?"

"Yep, and I saw you come within the breadth of a flea's nostril of going down yourself. Look here! You can't take on that whole flock all by yourself. They've figured out how to fight back."

I pointed out some rips and tears on the wings and tail where they had connected with claw or beak. "And that ain't all!" I said as I pointed out two splotches on the upper wing surface. "You might say they attacked you with both ends at once! If one of those organic bombs had hit you or the engine— well, you wouldn't be around to listen to me."

Arnold Bennett was unfazed by his narrow escape. "Can you fix it, Grandpappy? I sure want another crack at 'em!"

"In a day or so," I said. "But you can't fight all of them by yourself. You'd need a whole squadron to fight that many crows."

'Then let's put a squadron together," he replied.

"And just how do you propose we do that?"

"Grandpappy, you supply the planes. I'll supply the pilots."

VII.

This entire situation was getting way out of hand, I decided as I headed for town the next day. How did I go from the simple act of rescuing a little snake from a bunch of murauderous crows to building a squadron of World War I aircraft. I guess it goes to prove that life at Ruination Farm, even though it's clear out six miles south of Somewhere, is never dull.

But I picked up kits for three more planes. I decided not to play favorites, so I chose a French Spad XIII, a British Sopwith Camel and another German plane, an Albatross D-3. This was costing me a lot more than a shotgun and some shells—but I had never financed a war before, and I was kind of curious to see how it would turn out.

By the time I got back to the farm, Arnold Bennett had rounded up four more king snakes. They all seemed ready and eager to learn, so I set about assembling the new aircraft and repairing the Fokker D-7. Of course we were short one plane, since I hadn't counted on Arnold doing such a masterful job of recruiting.

"Listen up now!" I said to those snakes as they assembled in front of me "I know you can hear me, so don't pretend you're deaf. You volunteered for this, and I expect you to follow orders. Arnold Bennett here can be your squadron leader, but I'm in overall command. Is that clear?"

Five snaky heads nodded in agreement.

"Now we have five pilots and four planes here, so you'll have to take turns. That means each of you in turn will sit out every fourth patrol. Of course, that's if you're all good enough to make it through basic flight training."

Well, I needn't have worried about that. As it turned out, Arnold Bennett had a natural eye for talent. Apparently several dozen king snakes, two or three garter snakes and even one old rattlesnake that I didn't know was lurking about had all volunteered.

Arnold picked these four because, as he said, "They seemed to have the right stuff."

It seemed obvious to me that Arnold Bennett had the makings of a natural leader. So when I repainted his plane to cover the damage the crows had made, I added a tiny black crow to the fuselage. When he asked what it was for, I explained how fighter pilots would use them as markings to indicate how many enemy aircraft they had brought down.

"You mean I get one for every crow I knock out of the sky?" he asked.

"Yes. Get five and you can call yourself an ace." You see, Johnny. I wanted to know just how far that snake's ambition extended. Apparently it went quite a ways.

"I'll get a bunch," he promised, "but the one I want most is that old white devil!"

VIII.

Bright and early the next morning I started putting the four new snakes through basic flight training. Of course there was no manual to follow, as this had never been done before, to the best of my knowledge. So I just did what I thought was best, using the remote first to put each one through a series of loops, dives and rolls. I have to admit that a couple of them did look a little green around the nostrils the first time or two, but by the end of the second day I figured they were all ready to solo.

So far those four new snakes hadn't spoken a word to me. I guess old habits die hard. But when they saw their four planes lined up for takeoff the next morning, I could swear I heard a tiny "Hooray!" escape through four pairs of snaky little lips.

Arnold and three of his mates slithered into their cockpits, while the fourth stood by looking so sad that I promised him a special breakfast of grubs and worms while we waited for the patrol to return. This cheered him up, and he volunteered to spin the props with his own tail to start the engines.

"Contact!" I called out, and Arnold Bennett led his squadron into the air just as the first rays of sunlight poked over the tops of the Dismal Hills. And in that first light of dawn, I saw at least twenty crows take off from their roosts in the treetops to meet them. Apparently neither side was going to back down.

Now you might think that odds of five to one would be a mismatch, but crows are slow flyers and kinda clumsy in the air. Arnold Bennett seemed to know just where his strong points were, and he took full advantage of them. He led his four planes in a steep climb until they were a good hundred feet above that circling, cawing mob. Then, one at a time, they peeled off and dived.

The crows scattered each time a plane roared through that jumbled mass of black feathers, claws and beaks. Then they'd try to regroup and go after the plane. But before they could attack, another plane came screaming down at them. And by the time the fourth fighter had dived through their midst, Arnold Bennett had regained his altitude and was ready to dive again.

Now each dive forced that mob of crows down closer and closer to the Windy River, and this made the fight that much more dangerous for both sides.

Several great galloping catfish came up to the surface to watch, and they had more than just a passing interest. I could tell what they were thinking. *Breakfast will soon be served!*

The fight ended when Arnold Bennett got right above and behind a crow on his second dive, and he forced it down so low that one of it's wings struck the water. That was all it took. The poor crow splashed in and made one great galloping catfish very happy. I could swear I saw it waving its whiskers in thanks as Arnold zoomed back up for another dive. Of course that catfish would probably have been just as happy if the crow had bagged Arnold Bennett instead.

But when the crows saw one of their number go down, they decided they'd had enough and broke off the fight. They flew back to the trees on the far side of the Old Windy, and Arnold brought his squadron back to the corn patch. I checked each plane for battle damage. Aside from a rip on one upper wing and a couple of white splotches, there wasn't any.

But now, instead of one slither-strutting snake, I had four of them on my hands—not to mention a fifth so jealous that he developed a king-snake-size case of the mopes. Arnold Bennett didn't make things any easier by insisting that I paint another crow on his fuselage before he went up again. I humored him because I knew there wouldn't be any more fighting that day.

Those murauderous crows seemed completely demoralized, and maybe this war would come to an end with no further casualties on either side. But

I hadn't reckoned on the rhetorical powers of that old white devil that led them.

All that afternoon and far into the evening I could hear cawing from those oak trees on the far side of the Windy River, and it wasn't the usual jumble of casual conversation either. This sounded more like a speech, and I didn't need three guesses to know who was making it. That old white devil must have been a first-class orator. It wasn't long before I'd hear a tremendous "CAW!" from his audience every time he made a point. Whatever he was telling them, it sure sounded like they were buying it.

"Grandpappy," I told myself, "as sure as the green grapes ripen on the vine, there's going to be another fight tomorrow."

IX.

Since that old white crow had been speechifying to his troops, I thought it might be a good idea to give a little pep talk to my squadron. But I was sort of stuck for a subject. I mean, how do you motivate a bunch of snakes? Well, I needn't have worried. Those reptiles came up with a topic all on their own.

"Grandpappy," Arnold Bennett said as we gathered around my hearth that night, "my mates here would like to have names just like I do."

"Look here," I said. "They can't be *just* like yours. That defeats the whole purpose of a name, which is to give you an individual identity. Now you might have the same *last* name—Lampropeltis—since you're all king snakes and members of the same squadron. But your first names need to be different from each other."

"Then give us some different names." Arnold Bennett was a very persistent snake.

"All right then, Arnold. I named you after an English author. I probably should have used a German author, since you're flying a German plane—but I guess it's a little late for that now. But as for you," I added, pointing out the snake I'd assigned the Albatross D-3, "it's not too late. You need the name of a German author, so you will be known as Thomas Mann Lampropeltis. Is that okay by you?"

The snake nodded and brought the tip of his tail up to the side of his head in pretty snappy salute—pretty snappy for a snake, that is.

"You," I said to the Spad pilot, "can be Victor Hugo Lampropeltis, since both author and plane are French. And you," I said as I smiled at the Camel pilot, should be English, and that one is easy. You are William Shakespeare Lampropeltis."

But then I was stuck. The fifth snake did not have a plane of his own, and my budget would not permit a trip to town for another aircraft—not for a while, at least. So I did what I always do when I have a problem to think about. I brewed a pot of tea, sat in my favorite chair and set my brain to work while the rest of me relaxed. I had barely started the second cup when the answer came to me.

"Look here," I said to the fifth snake. "I can't rightly think of an author for you, but I can think of a character. You're a snake without an airplane, so I'll name you after *The Man Without a Country*. As I recall, his name was Phillip Nolan, so you are now Phillip Nolan Lampropeltis. How does that strike you?"

"He thinks it's just fine," said Arnold Bennett, who had apparently elected himself as spokesman for the squadron.

So early next morning, just as the sun peeped up over the tops of the Dismal Hills, Arnold Bennett led his squadron of four into the air. Phillip Nolan flew the Albatross, while Thomas Mann remained behind. As things turned out, that was lucky for Thomas Mann and very unlucky for Phillip Nolan.

I heard one sudden tremendous "CAW!" from the trees over on the far side of the Windy River as another flock of crows rose to meet them. And this time that old white devil led them himself!

Arnold Bennett was never shy about accepting a challenge. He led his squadron in a steep climbing turn to gain the height advantage on that flock. But that crafty old white devil had quietly sent *another* bunch into the air before dawn. They were now up almost clear out of sight and waiting to spring their trap.

Arnold Bennett and William Shakespeare tore right into that crow formation, which, just as the day before, broke apart to let them pass through. But when Victor Hugo peeled off, that second bunch pounced on poor Phillip Nolan.

I could see it coming, but there was nothing I could do to warn him. The high bunch followed him down, and the lower flock refused to break apart for him. There had to be a collision and, sure enough, there was. Another crow tumbled into the river and made another great galloping catfish very happy, while Phillip Nolan turned his plane for the bank and tried to glide it in with a dead engine.

Both mobs of crows were on him in a flash. That old white devil and four or five of his cronies landed right on the upper wings of the Albatross and used their combined weight to force it lower and lower. I had my fishing rod out by then, and the other snakes had regained height and were ready to dive again, but it looked hopeless. The Albatross was too far out for me to snag, and before Arnold and his mates could break through, the plane's wheels hit the water and in it went.

I lit out for one of the three or four dozen bends the Windy River makes as it winds its way past Ruination Farm. I knew just where the current would bring it close enough to shore for me to snag it, but that flock of crows was determined to thwart me. That old white devil cawed out a set of orders, and five or six of his mates sank their claws into the fabric of that plane. Then they all flapped as hard as they could, and would you believe it? They actually lifted the Albatross clear of the water!

It looked like they planned to carry it back to their lair as a trophy, and they might have done it if it hadn't been for Arnold Bennett and his remaining squadron mates. The three of them scattered the first flock of crows and then pounced on the bunch that was hijacking the Albatross.

Arnold aimed his Fokker straight for the old white crow, but that wily old rascal took off at the last instant, and Arnold clipped the crow next to him instead. The impact didn't stop Arnold's engine, but it did knock the crow into the water, and another great galloping catfish waved its whiskers in thanks. The other hijackers decided they'd had enough, dropped the Albatross and lit out for the far side of the river.

But it was too late for Phillip Nolan. When the crows lifted his plane clear of the water, that snake decided he'd rather take his chances in the river than wind up a prisoner of the crows. I can't say as I blame him, but oh my! Talk about being caught between a rock and a hard place or between Scylla and Charybdis!

(What's that? Well, look it up if you don't know what it means. The dictionary is right over there, and I'll wait until you find it. I like to make my stories instructive, even if I do get a *little* careless with the truth occasionally.)

Phillip Nolan found himself caught between crows and catfish and apparently thought his best chance was with the latter. So he slipped out of his harness and went over the side just as his mates could come to the rescue. He was a good strong swimmer—for a snake—but no match for a great galloping catfish. So the squadron suffered its first loss.

X.

Now you might think those snakes would be all sad and mopey after losing one of their mates, but that wasn't the case. No sir! They were all slithering and squirming with joy because I had managed to snag the plane and reel it in, and it looked like I could have it fixed and back in the air in a day or so. When I asked Arnold Bennett why they weren't mourning the loss of a mate, he explained it to me thus.

"Any snake alive would give the rest of its days for the adventure Phillip Nolan had. He got to *fly!* That's something that no snake, except for us, has ever done! He took a crow with him too—remember that! Now we won't have to leave anyone behind. Just get that plane fixed for Thomas Mann, and we'll have another crack at 'em tomorrow!"

I went to sleep that night thinking, *Grandpappy, what have you done?* King snakes are usually pretty placid critters and useful to have around, but this bunch had become absolutely bloodthirsty. Or at least Arnold Bennett had become that way. His mates loved the flying part, but they weren't quite so eager about mixing it up with the crows.

Still, by week's end Arnold Bennett had four crows to his credit. William Shakespeare had one, and Victor Hugo and Thomas Mann shared a crow between them. Add in the one poor Phillip Nolan had brought down, and that made seven crows transformed into catfish food. The crows seemed to be losing their taste for war. Apparently it's no fun when the other fellow can hit back.

But that old white devil would caw at them for half the night. I'd lie there in bed, listen to his speechifying and wonder what kind of foolishness he was preaching. It seemed his voice was growing hoarser and more desperate each night. Maybe they would soon tire of the fighting and call it quits. That would be fine with me, but Arnold Bennett did not share my feelings.

"You see," he told me one morning as the squadron gathered in front of my fireplace for its preflight meal of grubs and worms, "we have several million years of persecution at the hands of crows and other birds throughout our history, and we mean to do our part to square accounts. That's our mission."

"Your mission is to protect my corn patch," I reminded him.

"Not any longer," he said. "Those crows need to be taught a lesson. In fact, just about all birds do. What right do they have to go flying all over the sky while we're chained here to the ground?"

"What right do you have to go tinkering with Nature's eternal plan?" I replied.

"The rights we have are the rights we take. Isn't that so, mates?" The others nodded their agreement, but they weren't very enthusiastic about it. Maybe it was their upbringing that had warned them about speaking with humans—or maybe they were starting to develop a conscience.

"Speaking of rights," Arnold Bennett went on. "What right did those crows have to try to peck me to pieces?"

"We humans have a saying, Arnold. *Two wrongs do not make a right.* I know how mean birds can be to snakes. But as I recall, snakes have been known to rob bird's nests on occasion, haven't they?"

"Humans eat eggs too, don't they? Well, where do you think *those* eggs come from?" For a critter who had just started talking, Arnold was pretty handy with an argument. I could see how his ancestor might have persuaded Eve to munch that apple.

So I figured it was up to me to find a way to end this war, since I'd played a part in starting it. The two main problems were Arnold Bennett and that old white crow. If I simply grounded the squadron, the crows would have a free run at my corn patch. If I let Arnold and his mates mix it up over the river, they'd probably bag a few more crows. But eventually, one by one, the crows would pick them off.

So far the only clear winners were those great galloping catfish. Every morning they would come up to the surface to get themselves ringside seats for the fracas. I don't think they were rooting for either side. They just seemed to enjoy the free show and the complimentary breakfast that was likely to come with it.

The most likely solution was to get Arnold Bennett and that old white crow to go at it *mano a mano*, as the Spaniards say. If Arnold could bring him down, then I was pretty certain the war would end right there on the spot. Of course, the outcome might go the other way—in which case I would have to invest in a shotgun and some shells.

I knew that Arnold wouldn't mind a fair-and-square match with any of the crows, but that old white devil didn't seem to like putting his own feathers at risk. How could we lure him into a duel? I decided to lay the problem in Arnold Bennett's lap— or rather, in what passes for a lap in a snake's anatomy.

"Look here, Arnold," I said to him that evening. "You've got four crows painted on your fuselage. Get one more and you'll be an ace. No snake has ever done that. But the fifth one really ought to be special—one that will go down in legend, song and story." I wasn't sure if he knew what legends, songs and stories were, but the idea seemed to appeal to him.

"Do you mean that old white one, Grandpappy?"

"I did sort of have him in mind, yes."

"I'd like to get him more than any of the others, but he won't ever take me on in a fair fight. Do you remember when you saved me from that bunch that was trying to peck me to pieces?"

"I sure do. That's what started this whole mess."

"Well, that old white crow was behind it. He got the others to pounce on me, but he didn't jump in himself until I was pretty near helpless. That's the way he is in the air too. He keeps his flock around him all the time, and I can't get at him."

Well, all of a sudden the answer was obvious. "Arnold," I said, "if you can't get to him, then we'll have to make him come to you."

"How do we do that?" he asked.

"You just give a listen," I said. Then I told him what we would do.

XI.

Early the next morning I sent the squadron into the air as usual. As soon as they were clear of the corn patch and climbing, I saw the crows take off from their roosts in the trees across the river and come out to meet them. That old white rascal had been cawing at them most of the night, but I sensed a definite reluctance among his followers. I could summon up a little sympathy for the followers, but not for their leader. Sound carries only too well across the Windy River, and his cawing had kept me awake for two nights running.

Arnold and his mates flew in a tight circle, each protecting the tail of the plane ahead of him. Still keeping their circle formation, they slowly made their way out over the river to where the crows flew back and forth, wondering how to deal with this new tactic. They looked to their leader, and he seemed to be stumped.

And Johnny, that was just what I was hoping for.

Suddenly Arnold Bennett's engine quit! He turned for home and began a long glide back to a dead-stick landing on the riverbank. Would he make it all the way back? It looked like he just might. But then the old white crow made his move.

First he cawed out an order to his followers. Then he broke away from his mates and took after Arnold Bennett as fast as he could fly. The rest of that mob swarmed around the circling planes to hem them in and keep them from coming to Arnold's rescue. That was just what we had hoped for.

Arnold waited until that crow was almost on him. Then he restarted his engine, just like I had shown him the night before. The Fokker zoomed up in a steep climbing turn that put Arnold Bennett right square between that old white crow and his followers. Then he put the D-7's nose down and went straight for his adversary!

That old white devil realized just a moment too late that he had been tricked. He tried to sideslip, but Arnold Bennett was having none of that. He turned with the crow and the two met almost head on. I saw a puff of white feathers and then a flash of fire. That crow must have nicked the fuel line and spilled a little gas on the hot engine. Maybe just a drop, but that was all she needed. The Fokker D-7 was in flames by the time it hit the water where the great galloping catfish were waiting.

Through my binoculars I saw Arnold Bennett bring the tip of his tail up to his snaky forehead in a snappy salute. Then he went over the side just before his plane hit the water. The catfish were waiting, but they had positioned themselves between the crash and my side of the river, and Arnold Bennett lit out for the far bank instead. What with the smoke and the confusion—and the remains of that old white crow to squabble over—Arnold had a pretty good lead by the time they realized where he was heading and took out after him.

It was going to be an awfully close thing, but he seemed to have a slim chance of making it. I didn't watch the end of the race because there was nothing I could do to affect the outcome, and I wanted to believe that he made it. Maybe he did. Either way, his career as a pilot was over. He was either in the belly of a catfish or stuck on the far side of the river with no way to get back, and I wasn't about to go looking for him.

XII.

Of course that battle ended the war. The crows lost all desire for fighting after their leader went down, and my three remaining snakes found themselves back at the corn patch with a king-snake-size case of the mopes.

"What do we do now?" their spokesman hissed to me. (It was William Shakespeare, if you need to know.) "The fighting is over, and there's nothing left to fly for."

"Yes there is," I said. "Arnold Bennett may have made it to the far shore. If he did, he's stranded over there. Why don't you fly over and see if you can find him?"

"What if we don't?" hissed Victor Hugo.

That one stumped me for a couple of seconds. What *could* I do with a squadron of flying snakes now that I had no further use for them? I could see them getting into all kinds of trouble and bringing hordes of unwanted visitors out to Ruination Farm.

It was Thomas Mann who gave me the answer I needed. "There ought to be some way we could celebrate the end of the war," he said.

"Of course!" I replied. "You could fly on to Paris! That's where the human pilots went in World War I—the allied ones, that is. But I'm sure they would welcome you too, Thomas. The French have always loved heroes, and that's what you all are."

"But we don't know where Paris is," William Shakespeare pointed out.

"It's just a ways beyond the Dismal Hills," I assured him. "You'll know it when you see it. There's this big iron tower right in the center of it."

Of course I neglected to mention that it was several thousand miles beyond the Dismal Hills, and that their planes only carried enough fuel to make five or six of them. But the land beyond the Dismal Hills was smooth and flat, so they would land without crashing. I told them a few stories about Paris, and I'm afraid I got just a *little* careless with the truth a few times. But the upshot was that those snakes got so anxious to see that fabulous city that they forgot all about searching for Arnold Bennett. I'm afraid that loyalty does not rank very high on a snake's list of virtues.

This time William Shakespeare Lampropeltis led them into the air. They circled once, waved their wings to me, then flew out over the Windy River and headed straight for the Dismal Hills. I watched them until they were just tiny specks against the morning sky. Then I turned and walked back to the house, and dang if I could decide whether I felt relieved or lonely.

The Popapple Caper

Johnny, I want to give you a bit of absolutely sound advice. Be real careful about what you say and do when an old beggar woman comes to your door. They have what you might call a hidden agenda, and you could easily find yourself smack-dab in the middle of an adventure that you really wanted no part of. Let me tell you a tale from my own past that illustrates this point.

It was just a short time after I'd rid myself of those flying snakes and made peace with that flock of crows. I'd taken my boat across the Windy River and cleared a little patch of ground on the far side. There I had planted a miniature cornfield just for the crows. When they gathered around to see what I was up to, I told 'em this corn patch was for crows only, and if they left mine alone, I'd see to it they had their own little corn patch every year. They let on like they didn't understand, but I knew they could.

To show that it was just for them, I whittled out a huge crow from a bit chunk of poplar, painted it black and set it up in the middle of their field as a

43

scarehuman. I told them it was a sign that this was their field and no one else had better mess with it. They really appreciated that little touch, and from then on I never had any trouble with crows.

So I was able to harvest a good crop of popping corn after all, and that fall I took some to the Snodgrass County Fair. I calculated that this was the year I would beat out old Orville Whatshisname for the blue ribbon. But wouldn't you know it? He edged me out again! The judges told me it was close—that I'd come nearer to out-popping him than any challenger had for years—but he still got the blue and I had to settle for second.

It was uncharitable of me to think it, but I suspected old Orville had greased those judges with something a little greener and more persuasive than butter. Yes, I hang my head in shame that I harbored such thoughts, but there they were. That contest was rigged, and there was no way I could win it honestly. And I was *not* going to play dirty! No sir!

"Dingbust and dadblast!" I said as I put up the red ribbon. "I'd give just about anything for a chance to win that competition fair and square."

Well, no sooner had I said those words than there came a knock at my door. It wasn't any shy, hesitant kind of tap either. Whoever sought my attention had a real set of knuckles on him—or her, as it turned out.

"Great galloping catfish!" I exclaimed. "Someone is without and wants within!"

Yes, I was surprised, and for good reason too. As you recall, Ruination Farm is clear out eight miles south of Somewhere, twelve miles east of Elsewhere and well off the main highway. Visitors are a mighty rare occurrence, so you can bet that knock startled the blue jimhickies out of me. But I am not one to leave a visitor out in the cold—though as I recall, it was a fairly warm day. I threw open the door and called out, "Come on in!" before I even had a good look at who it was.

She didn't need a second invitation. A little old woman, dressed like a character in an old-time Punch and Judy show, marched right in and plopped herself down in my favorite chair like she was some long-lost relation. But she was no relative I could remember. Fact is, I'd never set eyes on her before.

"Thank you, Sir. You are most kind," she said in a voice that reminded me of a character being played by a so-so actress. "It is many a long day I have traveled this road with never a friendly word or an offer of help from anyone."

"Is that a fact?" I said, trying to keep the sarcastic chuckle down in my innards. "What kind of help do you seek, may I ask?" I figured that if she was a character from some sort of play, the best way to deal with her was to become one myself.

"Just a cup of tea and a little something to eat and perhaps a few minutes to rest before I resume my weary way," she replied.

"The tea is no trouble, and you're welcome to the use of that chair," I said. "I'll fetch a footstool so you can prop your feet up. What do you fancy in the way of victuals?"

"Beggars really shouldn't be choosers," she said. Aha! She was going to test me.

"Go ahead and wish," I told her. "I can't promise to fulfill it, but I'll do the best I can." See, Johnny, when dealing with an old beggar woman, you have to make her show her hand before you show yours. She proceeded to do just that.

> "Oh macaroni and cheese with honey from bees.
> Some french-fried potatoes or dutch-
> fried tomatoes.
> Or a plate of chop suey, all cooked nice and gooey.
> Or leftover stew with some grapefruit juice too.
> Something roasted or something toasted,
> Like a bit of ham or lamb with jam."

She recited that all on one breath, which impressed me. Then she added, "Anything like that will do. I really don't want to put you to any trouble."

That, of course, was an untruth. The whole purpose of a rhyming test is to stir up troubles, problems, predicaments and general unease. But I knew how to deal with it. "No trouble at all," I assured her. I slipped the footstool under her feet and spread a blanket over her peculiar costume as she settled back in the chair. Then I set to work in the kitchen. To refuse an old beggar woman's request was to court the worst kind of peril, as you may know if you have read any of the old folktales.

I had barely started my preparations when I heard a "ZZZZNORRK" from the chair. That old woman was snoring away like she hadn't slept for weeks. Maybe she hadn't. From the pitch, tone and volume, I figured I was in for at least a two-hour concert. It was enough to spoil the spinach right on the spot.

"Why do they all have to come here?" I asked myself as I worked. That old beggar woman could just as easily have gone up the road to my nearest neighbors, the Finsters, or west a ways to the Jenkins place. But I suppose, being endowed with the powers that wise old beggar women were supposed to have, she probably knew in advance what her reception would be like at either of those places.

You see, the Finsters were more than just an ordinary family. They *radiated* ordinariness. Or to put it another way, ordinariness coated Fred, Frances and their two children like teflon, and nothing out of the ordinary could get within a quarter-mile of their household. In fact, they were odds-on favorites to be chosen as one of the Ten Most Ordinary Families in America. I'm not sure if that's an honor or not, but they seemed to think it was, and they gloried in it in an ordinary sort of way.

The two Jenkins boys did have an IQ of about 150, but unfortunately those 150 points were divided more or less evenly between them. Their lights did not shine all that brightly, I'm afraid, and a wise old beggar woman from folklore would look and feel as out of place among the Jenkins as snow in July.

So I guess that left me and Ruination Farm.

Granny's nap lasted just over two hours, which gave me enough time to whip up a pretty decent plate of grub for her. I fixed a little something for myself too, since it's impolite to make a guest eat alone. Besides, cooking tends to make me hungry.

Just as I finished dishing up her plate, she gave one last great "ZZZNORRK!" and her eyes popped open. "Oh dear! Oh dear! Oh dear! Oh dear!" she cried as I set down her plate. "I must have over-slept myself! I will not be able to enjoy this wonder-ful repast you have set before me!"

"Well, I'm sorry you won't have time to eat, but I didn't want to wake you," I said as I reached for the plate. But the old woman grabbed it first.

"I said I wouldn't have time to *enjoy* it," she told me. "I didn't say I wouldn't have time to eat it." And with those words, if you can believe it, she opened her mouth wider than any mouth has a right to open and slid that whole plateful right down her gullet all at once! It was pretty hot too, but that didn't seem to faze her one bit. Then she let loose a tre-mendous belch and said, "Thank you! I'm sure it would have been delicious."

That old woman must have had cast-iron plumb-ing inside her.

"Wait a minute!" I said as she started for the door. "Aren't you forgetting something?"

"Huh? What? Oh yes!" she said somewhat sheep-ishly. "Thank you for reminding me. I'm rather new at this, you see."

Actually, she looked pretty old to be new at any-thing, but I let that pass. She stuck her hand into a pocket in her tattered old Punch-and-Judy skirt, pulled out the strangest apple I ever did see, and presented it to me with a flourish while adding the following verse.

"Here is the answer to your wish.
It will make a most incredible dish.
But use it wisely, for better or worse,
For it may be a blessing or it may be a curse."

With that, she flounced out of the house, slammed the door behind her and left me holding an apple and wondering what she meant.

II.

I just stood there for a while, pondering her words and then pondering that apple. At least it *seemed* to be an apple. It was about the size of a baseball and round like a baseball too. Its color was the palest red I ever saw on an apple, practically pink in fact. It could almost be a ripening tomato, but it was harder than any tomato I ever held.

"Well," I said to myself, "let's cut it open and see what we have."

I took a paring knife to it and soon discovered it was also the toughest apple I ever tried to cut. When I finally had it halved, I saw the inside was practically all seeds—or pips, I should say. There was just a little rim of flesh inside the skin, and those pips were the same pale pinkish-red as the skin.

"Well, if that ain't enough to wiggle the watercress!" I said wonderingly. I took a piece I had trimmed and sniffed it. It did smell like an apple, but it was the most pungent apple I ever sniffed. I touched my tongue to it, and the taste was like unfrozen juice concentrate. It was so strong it was practically bitter. What was I supposed to do with an apple like that?

I pondered that question while I attempted to coax old Hairball out from under my bed, where he had fled at the first knock. I believe I hinted that my cat was a little paranoid. Well, that's an understatement. He's a dumpoff cat from the city, you see, and not used to country ways.

All right, Johnny. I knew you were going to ask what a dumpoff cat is. It's a city cat that city folks decide they don't want to care for anymore, but they're too softhearted to kill it themselves. So they drive it way out in the country, dump it off and let nature do the job for them. Maybe they talk themselves into believing the poor critter will survive and even prosper, but of course it won't. Nature can be mighty cruel to critters who don't know its rules, and city cats don't.

I remember the night Hairball arrived. I was in bed asleep when the sound of a racing engine woke me. I heard the screech of brakes, the slam of a door and then the car roared off again. "That's a cat being dumped, as sure as the Lord made little green artichokes," I said to myself. "Let's see if he has sense enough to head for my door. If he does, then there's hope for him."

He did and there was. Five minutes later I heard a *"Meow!"* at my front door and Hairball walked into my life. So he survived, but he wasn't quite prospering yet. Transplanted city cats have more neuroses than old Freud could have shaken a stick at. I suspect having to live with humans causes most of them.

To Hairball, a strange knock at the door meant the cat police coming to take him to the Shelter, where he would be sheltered right out of the remainder of his nine lives. I was still trying to convince him that he was safe at Ruination Farm, but that weird old woman's appearance had set his therapy back by at least two weeks.

"It's all right, Old Fella," I said as I coaxed the poor critter out from under the bed. "Whoever she was, she's gone now, and she's not likely to show herself around these parts again."

As a folklore scholar, I should have known better. Mysterious old women *always* return at least once.

III.

I spent the rest of the day in a serious study of that apple and the mysterious old woman's strange warning. What did she mean by it being either a blessing or a curse? As far as that goes, what use was it at all? You couldn't eat it. There wouldn't be enough juice to drink, and what would the pips do except produce more apples just like it? Yet if an old beggar woman comes by speaking riddles in rhyme, there's sure to be some truth hidden in what she says. But where? It was enough to give a man a bad case of the blue jimhickies.

By the next day Hairball had recovered some of his composure, but I was still pondering, and pondering makes a person hungry after a while. So I got down a jar of my red-ribbon popcorn from the fair and set out my popper. "Dad gum and ding blast!" I said to the cat (for that's as close as I come to cursing). "What does Old Orville Whatshisname have that I lack? I *know* my stuff is as good as his!"

Hairball, as you might expect, made no answer. But I was so upset over the injustice of it all that I spilled some kernels on the counter, right where I'd halved that apple the day before.

I don't believe in wasting anything, so I gathered up the spilled kernels and dropped them in the popper with the others. And Johnny, that's what solved the riddle behind that peculiar apple.

You see, I must have scooped up a pip along with the kernels and dropped it in the popper with them. Thank goodness it was only one! In just a few seconds, KA-BLAMM! The popper's lid blew right off! I hit the floor and rolled under the table as *Ka-ping! Ka-pang! Ka-pong! Ka-pung!* Something ricocheted around the room. I heard the tinkle of broken crockery and knew that one of my teacups had been hit. Then came a *Thwump!* Like a hard fastball hitting a catcher's mitt. Whatever it was had smacked into my old overstuffed sofa and that had stopped it. I waited a minute to be sure and then crawled out to inspect the damage. Hairball was back under the bed again.

Lying on my sofa was a huge piece of popcorn— or was it popcorn? It was the size of a large cantaloupe and the same pale red color as that apple. I picked it up and found it was still warm to the touch. The smell was like a fresh, hot apple pie. "Let's try the old taste test," I said and then took a bite.

The taste was pure apple pie, but it dissolved in your mouth like cotton candy. The surface was just sticky enough to hold a coating of sugar and cinnamon, so I mixed some up, rolled this strange object in it, and sampled. *Dee*-licious!

But what should I call it? Well, it tasted like an apple, but it popped like corn—so I decided to call it a popapple. All of a sudden I realized something else. I was holding pure gold in my hands!

"Orville Whaterveryournameis," I said with a smile. "I do believe you have met your match at last!"

IV.

Of course there was one little engineering problem I needed to solve before the object in my hands could be turned into money in the bank account. The taste was wonderful, but the manufacturing process was downright dangerous. How could I pop this stuff without destroying my house in the process?

After cleaning up the mess this first popapple had made, I concluded that further experiments should be conducted outdoors. So I built a fire in the barbecue pit, greased up an old skillet and set it over the fire. Then I dropped in one of the smaller popping pips and stood back to await developments. They happened rather quickly.

With a *Crack!* that sounded like a small firecracker exploding, that pip shot into the air, blossoming out as it went. At about fifty or sixty feet it stopped, hung there in the sky for a second or so and then began to drop back to earth. I got under it just like the punt returner I used to be, threw up my hand for the fair catch and gathered it in just before it hit the ground.

(Yes, I was a return man for the old Cardinals before they moved to Arizona—before they even moved to St. Louis. Back when they were the old Chicago Cardinals—though modesty compels me to add that I only played one season for them before I had to quit because of a knee injury.)

When I caught it, that pip had expanded to roughly the size and shape of a football. But when I rolled it in cinnamon and sugar, it sure tasted a lot better than any football. At least I assume it did, never having had the experience of biting into a football.

Then I set the skillet closer to the fire and dropped in one of the biggest pips and jumped back as quickly as I could—and I was just in time too!

Blamm! This time the explosion sounded like a small bomb going off. The skillet itself jumped a foot or so, and that pip took off like a rocket almost straight up and expanding as it went. It was close to two hundred feet up and the size of a basketball when it lost momentum and began to drop back to earth. I wasn't all that sure I wanted to get under it for the catch.

But I caught it, and it was all warm and savory and seemed to be begging, "Roll me in sugar and cinnamon and gorge yourself, because I'm about the best dessert you're ever going to taste!"

It was too. But that still left me with the popping problem unresolved. You see, corn popping is considered an indoor activity, so I guessed that most folks would like to do their apple popping indoors as well. Standing out in the wind, rain or snow waiting for a popapple to drop from the sky and hoping you can catch it—that just wouldn't appeal to most folks.

"Grandpappy," I said to myself, "there's no two ways about it. You are going to have to design and build the world's first apple popper."

The easiest thing would be to have a device you could use in a fireplace or wood stove. But that would mean sending the pip right up the chimney or smokestack and who would want a popapple all covered with soot and ash? No, it would have to be a free-standing design worthy of my name and reputation.

My first thought was to work with what was already at hand, so I rummaged through the attic. (*Dang!* I'm going to have to clean that place out someday!) Finally I found the old sousaphone I carried when I hoofed it with the Snodgrass County Marching Band back in my younger days. I think you know those things—sort of like a tuba that somebody unwound and reshaped so it goes up your back, past your shoulder and over your head. I was good enough to be considered a virtuoso on the instrument—though modesty compels me to admit that old John Phillip Sousa was just a bit better.

Next I stretched one end of a length of rubber tubing over where the mouthpiece goes. Then I stuck the other end over the spout of my strongest copper teakettle. Then I dropped in a pip, secured the lid with baling wire and set the kettle on the stove. Finally I shouldered the sousaphone, pointed the bell at my overstuffed sofa, braced myself and waited for things to happen. They soon did.

BLU-DOOOT!

The note was a beautiful e-flat major, but the force of it broke another teacup and rattled all the windows. My cow went dry right on the spot. Old Hairball shot out from under the bed, through an open window and up my sycamore tree, where he stayed for the rest of the day. And would you believe it? My hens laid pre-scrambled eggs for the next week! So much for adapting what I already had. I was going to have to design and build the contraption from scratch.

I began with a sketch pad and a head full of ideas and finally wound up with a design that consisted of a length of clear plastic tubing, twisted round and round like a coil of rope and gradually expanding in diameter as it went. It reminded me a bit of an upside-down cone, with the top blossoming out like the bell on my sousaphone. I would have to make another trip to town to get the makings—and you know I'm stuck out here twelve miles west of Wherever. But if it meant a chance to snatch the blue ribbon away from old Orville Whatshisname, it would be worth the trip.

So I set out early the next morning, just as the sun was poking up over the Dismal Hills. I got lucky and found just what I needed in Wherever, and headed back to Ruination Farm chuckling with anticipation at what I would build.

It took three days of hard work to cut and mold and shape that plastic into the design I had sketched. I decided to make it in sections that could be pulled apart for cleaning and transportation and then reassembled when you were ready for business. It would take some strong clamps to hold things together when that popapple came shooting through, but all those twists and turns would slow it down and make it a bit more catchable.

Catching the finished product presented another problem. I couldn't haul my old sofa with me everywhere I went. I thought about using a catcher's mitt or maybe one of those oversize mitts that hockey goalies use, but I decided against them. Maybe I was still agile enough to catch a popapple on the fly, but your average eighty-year-old granny would find it more of a challenge.

But the hockey mitt did give me an idea. There's a net around the goal to stop the puck that can come in at more than a hundred miles an hour. So I called up a couple of my buddies from the old days when I played a couple of seasons with the Ottawa Senators—though modesty compels me to add that I was only second string—and they sent me some net that was guaranteed to stop one of Gretzke's slap shots.

Things were starting to fall into place.

All the while I was assembling my popper, I was thinking about the pips as well. I only had one popping apple, and I wasn't likely to get another. When those old beggar women leave, they vanish. It's no good trying to find them and order new supplies. I was going to have to be awfully careful with those pips.

I figured the best thing would be to plant a few right away and see how fast they grew. It was right about planting time anyway, and I had already cleared another small patch of ground down by the river. So I went out early the next morning with about a dozen of those little pips and proceeded to plant the world's first popapple crop.

That morning I discovered just how dangerous those pips could be.

V.

I'd put about six or seven pips in the ground and covered them with that good rich bottomland soil when one of the crows flew over from the trees on the far side to see what I was up to. He was just a youngster, and I'm sure he didn't mean any real harm. He was just full of mischief, as young crows tend to be.

Whatever the reason, he waited until my back was turned. Then, quick as anything, he jabbed his beak into the hole I had just filled and pulled out a freshly-planted pip. I turned just in time to see him tilt his head back and swallow it down.

"Shoo! You pestiferous crow!" I shouted as I waved my arms. He just cawed and started back across the river, but he never made it.

I heard a muffled *Whump!* and that crow seemed to swell up like a balloon suddenly filled with compressed air. That crow's innards must have been hot enough to make that pip explode. It must have expanded to roughly the size of a honeydew melon, and that's a lot more than your average crow's innards can handle. The results sure weren't pretty, and I won't go into detail here. Just imagine a balloon that suddenly gets too much compressed air, and you'll get the picture. Some great galloping catfish got an unexpected breakfast that morning.

Now your average crow is even more paranoid than old Hairball, and that particular bunch became instantly positive that I had invented some diabolical weapon to do them all in. So I had to row over to the far side and tell them all about those popapple pips and how dangerous they could be. But they still weren't convinced it was just an accident.

"All right," I told them. "It pains me to do it, but let me get a few things and I'll give you a demonstration."

I took some hamburger from the refrigerator, held it in my hand long enough to take the chill out of it, loaded three pips into it and molded it into a ball that would slide real easy-like down the gullet of a great galloping catfish. Then I rowed out to the middle of the river (with two crows perched as observers on the prow of my boat) and tossed the hamburger overboard.

Johnny, I felt right sorry for the catfish that rose to the bait. I don't enjoy taking the life of any of the Lord's critters, but I told myself this was all for the greater good. Besides, that great galloping catfish had a choice. It didn't have to grab that loaded hamburger—but of course it did.

That catfish waved its whiskers in thanks just before it slid back below the surface, which didn't make me feel any better about what I had just done. I started counting slowly, "One thousand one…one thousand two…" I had just reached one thousand six when the explosion came.

It was a bit more muffled this time. But the boat shook from stem to stern, and a column of water rose into the air as if a depth charge had gone off—which, in a manner of speaking, it had. In fact, all three of those pips must have fired at the same instant.

Then the catfish, or what was left of it, broached the surface. Fortunately, it was only for a few seconds, since it wasn't a very pretty sight. Two other catfish came up beside it, grabbed hold of the remains and hauled them back down to the bottom. I do not think their intentions were to hold a memorial service either. Brotherly or sisterly affection is pretty well unknown among great galloping catfish, and they do always seem to be blessed with a keen appetite.

But at least the crows got the message loud and clear. They took off for the trees on the far side, and I heard some mighty determined cawing throughout the day. So I figured my crop would be safe from raiding crows from then on. Now all I had to do was wait to see if those pips would grow into anything.

A small part of me actually hoped they wouldn't. Those popapples were delicious, but very dangerous too. That's a bad combination to turn loose on the general public.

VI.

They grew all right, though not the way I thought. I expected some tiny trees, since that's what apple pips grow into when you plant them. However, the popapples came up as vines, almost like tomatoes. And they came up fast too. It looked like I would have a crop before autumn rolled around.

Of course I put up a good strong varmint fence around those vines, more to protect the varmints than the crop, though. I sure didn't want a bunch of exploding possums or groundhogs on my hands! Apparently, though, the crows had spread the word that this particular fruit was not to be messed with.

So I never lost a single apple. I didn't have to deal with any exploding critters either.

All the while those vines were growing, I was tinkering with my apple popper. Finally I developed a working model that I felt I could take to the fair and demonstrate. It did look kind of funny, I have to admit. In fact, people would probably laugh at it at first. But that happened to Edison, Fulton and Marconi, so I was in good company. Besides, the last laugh is the one that really counts. I planned on having that.

Just to make sure the contraption would work, I hooked it up a few days before the fair and gave it what you might call a test run. I had decided not to use electricity with this particular model. So I set it on a small burner which I could light with a match.

Then I set up the net, fired up the burner, set it under the popping chamber and dropped a single pip down the spout (since I figured that one at a time was all that popper could handle safely) and stood back to await the result. I have to admit it was kind of spectacular.

Boom! The popper shook with the force of the explosion, but it held together. That expanding pip zipped through the spiral tubing and shot out the end with the size and velocity of a fast-pitch softball. Then it slammed into that hockey net and came to rest all golden brown and just waiting to be coated with cinnamon and sugar.

"Grandpappy," I said to myself, "you have done it again!"

Now only one question remained. What was I going to call this contraption? After careful consideration, I came up with Grandpappy's Peerless Powerful Pipapopper (or as an alternative Peerless Powerful Popapipper). I figured either one would do the trick.

Johnny, I'm afraid I got all dreamy at this point. I just closed my eyes and saw in my mind all those infomercials, with me handing out sugary chunks of fresh popapple to smiling, eager children, while parents reached for their credit cards and got set to dial the 800 number. I had it made. I was going to be far richer and more famous than old Orville Whatshisname ever thought of being. Why, I might even make the front cover of *People*!

Do you know something, Johnny? I forgot to ask myself one simple question. *Did I really want all that to happen?*

VII.

Well, the big day finally came, and I loaded the Peerless Powerful Pipapopper (or Popapipper), along with a small sack of the best and brightest pips into my truck and set off for the Snodgrass County Fair. Johnny, that fair is an *occasion*, let me tell you! Why, it looked like the whole darn county was there—along with half the population of our five neighboring counties as well.

I knew one person who would be there—old Orville Whatshisname—and I knew he would be ready to defend his title for the umteenth time. Sure enough, when I walked into the Agricultural Products Pavilion, there he was—setting up a brand-new popper and boasting to everyone within earshot about this new hybrid strain of corn he'd developed. He was positive it would win him yet another blue ribbon.

Or so he thought.

I guess I'd thrown a king-size scare into him the year before by finishing so close behind him. It looked like he was taking no chances this year. He gave me a smile and offered his hand, but it was the kind of handshake two boxers give each other just before they start throwing punches.

But I just smiled and started setting up the Peerless Powerful Pipapopper. Orville just stared at it and went all goggle-eyed.

"What kind of a corn popper is that?" he demanded.

"It's not exactly a corn popper," I told him. "As a matter of fact, I won't be popping corn this year, so you'll get your blue for Best Popcorn of the Year. But I do plan to ace you out for the big one—Best Overall Agricultural Product."

"We'll see about that!" he answered me, and went back to setting up his own popper and measuring out some corn for it. Meanwhile, I cleared a place for the popapple-catcher and made sure the net was anchored good and tight to the frame. Old Orville and the other contestants stopped their own preparations to watch me, and they all must have thought I'd lost about half my kernels since last year's competition.

Then the judges called us to out places and said, "Gentlemen, start your poppers and good luck to all of you!"

Old Orville just smirked and poured in his premeasured batch, and all but one of his competitors did the same. That one, of course, was me. Those other poor fellows had that already-defeated look about them, like they knew the only battle was for second place. I just stood there with one tiny pip in my hands and watched while they fumed and fussed over their fixings.

Of course, Orville's corn was the first to pop, and I had to admit it looked mighty impressive as it came cascading out of his popper and into the bowl. He had his own special blend of butter and seasoning ready for it as soon as the flow stopped, and I guess you could have counted the unpopped kernels on the fingers of two hands and still had your thumbs left over.

The judges looked at each other and nodded like they already had their minds made up. Then they looked at me and scratched their heads, because all this time I hadn't moved a muscle.

"Gentlemen and Honorable Judges," I said to them. "Please observe—but do take care to keep clear of the net!" Then I dropped my single pip into the popping chamber.

Boom! Whizz! By the time that pip cleared the end of the spiral tubing, it was the size of a small melon. Then it shot a measured twelve feet in a straight line and landed smack in the center of the net, just as I had planned. You see, I'd carved some grooves on the inside of that tubing, just like rifling in a gun barrel, to increase the accuracy when I fired.

"What kind of popcorn is *that*?" the judges all demanded.

"It's not popcorn at all," I informed them. "Gentlemen, before you stands my Peerless Powerful Pipapopper—or Popapipper, if you wish. What

I am about to give you is something absolutely unique—a popapple!" And with that, I whipped out a paring knife, sliced off some chunks, rolled them in cinnamon and sugar and passed them out to the judges.

"Amazing!" cried the first.

"Stupendous!" added the second.

"Needs just a bit more sugar," commented the third.

"Fire it off again," said the fourth. "I'll need another taste just to be sure."

By this time a crowd had gathered, and I had to shoo them away from the net before I could take aim and drop in another pip.

Pow! Went the pipapopper.

"*Oooohh!*" cried the crowd as the pip shot through the spiral tubing, out the muzzle and into the net. A small boy grabbed it and fetched it to me for fixing. "It's all warm and sticky—just like my grandma's apple pie!" he exclaimed.

Well, I had to pop, slice and fix eight more pips in rapid order before that crowd was satisfied. After the eighth shot, the tubing was getting a little too warm for safety. So I had to tell the crowd that was all for now, but please come back in a little while and I would have some to sell at a reasonable price—reasonable to me, that is.

They drifted off with that disappointed yet eager look on their faces—the kind that says, *"I'll be back, and I'll bring my money with me!"* But what really made my day was the way they treated old Orville Whatshisname. Not a single soul took a sample of his corn or asked for his autograph. After I fired off my pipapopper, it was like he didn't even exist.

Well, one of the judges did tell him, "Oh, by the way, you did win the corn popping contest. We'll get you the ribbon tomorrow." But he was busily chewing his fourth chunk of popapple as he spoke, so his words were kind of hard to understand.

Poor Orville looked as stricken as a child who had come down with the chicken pox on the morning of his big birthday party. Here he had put all that work into developing what was probably the best popcorn in the country, and all he got for his effort was, "Oh, by the way, you did win the *minor* league championship." Did I feel any pity for him? Not one bit, Johnny! Not one bit!

VII.

Now the Greater Snodgrass County Fair is a two-day event. On the first day the judges do their judging, and on the second they award the prizes, ribbons, medals, trophies and whatever. By the end of the first day, I figured I had a lock on several of the above. So when I went home that night, I made plans to bring back a full jar of pips. I planned on doing some serious cash business on the second day.

That night, instead of dreaming, I did mathematical sums in my head. One popapple could be sliced into how many pieces? Should I make them all the same size or sell them in different sizes with a different price for each? Do I charge everyone the same rate or have different prices for children and senior citizens? Should I sell the unpopped pips or only the finished product? Should I charge extra for the cinnamon and sugar?

Johnny, being successful brings its own set of complications with it.

The first complication came early the next morning just as I got to the pavilion. Something didn't smell quite right, and the closer I got to my place, the stronger that smell became. It wasn't hard to find the culprit. I followed my nose to one little piece of popapple, left over from yesterday, that I had sealed in a freezer bag and stuck under the counter to see how it would keep overnight.

Well, I had my answer. I had to tote that bag clear across the fairgrounds to the farthest garbage can I could find, and then use a whole can of air-freshener before my spot was usable again. If I sold the pips, I would have to include a warning label. *This product must be eaten fresh and eaten fast!* Just like that manna from heaven, I suppose.

But I figured that was just a minor complication. By the time that fair opened for business, my spot smelled fresh again, the pipapopper was all greased and ready to go, the cinnamon and sugar were out and my change box all ready to take in the dollars. I decided to forego credit card sales for the time being.

Old Orville had moved his operations clear down to the far end of the pavilion, where he sat with his back to me so that he wouldn't have to see the paying customers lining up. Now I know it was unchristian and uncharitable of me, but his misery made me downright happy. After all these years when he'd lorded it over the rest of us, he was finally eating crow instead of popcorn.

My morning passed in a swirl of activity. Word had gotten out that Old Grandpappy had something that had to be tasted to be believed. Why, the customers crowded around so thickly the other poppers had to be moved to another table just to give me room enough to operate.

Johnny, I'd fire off that pipapopper once every two or three minutes. I'd station a kid beside the net to fetch the popapple back to me, and I'd slice off a little sliver for him (or her—I'd change kids every two or three shots). Then I'd cut the rest of it up for the cash customers, and oh my! There sure were plenty of them. By eleven o'clock the line stretched clear out the door of the pavilion!

In fact, it was too much business for me to handle by myself. It was soon obvious I was going to need an assistant to help make change and keep the sugar and cinnamon bowls full. But where was there someone I knew and could trust?

Then I saw a familiar face. Young Abner Jenkins, my nearest neighbor out by Ruination Farm, was standing off to one side chewing on a piece of straw and watching me with an expression like—well, it's kind of hard to describe Abner's expression. His face sort of reminded me of a motel sign with *Vacancy* lit up in bright red neon letters. I suppose a thought might cross his mind every six months or so. But he's totally honest, and he always does exactly what you tell him to do.

So I called him over and said, "Help me out for a while, if you've got nothing better to do. I'll pay you a few dollars, and you can take a slice off every second or third popapple the kids fetch back to me."

That made him think, which is not something he's had much practice at. Finally he looked at me kind of shy-like and said, "That be enough for a hot dog?"

"I'll make certain you have enough for a hot dog, Abner," I assured him. "In fact, I'll give you enough to get two of them. Three, if you really do a good job."

See, Johnny, when you negotiated with Abner Jenkins, you had to do it in ways he understood. Money never meant anything to him, but hot dogs sure did. So I gave him some latex gloves and the knife, and he did the cutting and coating while I fired off the pipapopper and took in the money.

With Abner's help I got my firing time down to about once a minute, but after another hour the pipapopper was getting hot to the touch and I was more than a mite hungry. In fact, I was ready to announce that I'd be shutting down for a while and taking Abner to lunch, when two very important-looking individuals pushed their way through the crowd and stepped up to my table.

One of them was my friend Myer O'Dwyer, Chairman of the Fair and President of the Greater Snodgrass County Chamber of Commerce. "Well, Grandpappy," he said, "it looks like you're the hit of the fair this year."

"It appears that way," I answered as modestly as I could. All the while I was thinking, *who is this other fellow? He looks to be even more important than Myer.*

Myer answered my question by presenting me with a card and saying, "Grandpappy, allow me to present Mr. Leonardo Monebaggio from Depoquet & Monebaggio, the giant international food con-glomerate."

I looked at the card and silently changed the name to Deep Pockets and Moneybags. What, I wondered, was somebody that important doing out at our little old county fair? Myer O'Dwyer soon enlightened me.

"We came out here to talk with Orville Whatshisname," he explained. "But when we saw the crowd around your table, we just had to see what interested them so much."

"Well, I'm glad you stopped by. Abner, cut this next popapple in two and give half to each of these gentlemen." And with that I loaded up the pipapopper and fired it again.

"Amazing!" Mr. Moneybags cried when he sampled the finished product. "Could you close down for an hour or so? We want to take you to lunch and make you some offers that you can't possibly refuse."

I agreed and then spoke to my new assistant. "Abner, I'm going to lunch with these gentlemen. Now here's what I want you to do." Then I gave him strict orders (and with Abner, they have to be strict) that he was just to sit there and keep an eye on things. He was to tell the customers that I would be back after lunch and guard my supply of pips. Above all he was not—and I repeated, *NOT*—to try using the pipapopper himself.

"In fact, Abner," I concluded, "I don't even want you to touch it. Keep things safe until I come back, and then I'll buy you all the hot dogs you can hold. Fair deal?"

"Fair deal, Grandpappy. You can count on me," he said—and I believed him.

Johnny, that was one of the biggest mistakes I ever made.

VIII.

"Sir," Mr. Moneybags said as soon as we were seated in food court in the center of the pavilion and the waiter had taken our orders. "It is not just a shame. Why, it is almost a *crime* that more than ninety-nine percent of the Great American Public is denied access to your wonderful product!"

Since attendance at the Greater Snodgrass County Fair was considerably less than one percent of the population of America, I was forced to admit that he had a point. Moneybags was all smiles, but there was a look in his eye that I didn't quite like—friendly and yet not friendly—like the look a cat might give a bird while he tries to think of a way to get just a little closer.

"Let's just cut right to the chase," I said, because I wanted to get the business out of the way before the chow arrived. Trying to negotiate while I'm eating always makes me grouchy. Tends to give me heartburn too.

"Very well," he said. "We can market you, Grandpappy. We can put your—what do you call those things, anyhow?"

"*Popapple* is the name I came up with."

"Hmm. We may have to work a bit on that. But whatever we choose to call 'em, we can mass market you from coast to coast and border to border.

And did I mention that we have an international distribution network too? Well, we do. It could mean millions for you, Sir! Tens of millions, in fact! Forget that old guy with the popcorn and the funny name. You'll be right up there with the movie stars and the sports celebs!"

"Don't know for sure if I'd want all that," I told him.

"You *wouldn't* want to be rich and famous? Why, Sir, that's almost un-American!" Johnny, I swear that man looked as shocked and disappointed as a kid who's just discovered that Santa Claus is really Uncle Floyd in a rented suit.

"I consider myself pretty rich right now," I said. "You see, I have all the money I need. Not always all that I *want*," I admitted (because I do believe in being honest, despite what you may think sometimes). "But I really do have all that I need."

But old Monebaggio (or Moneybags, as I like to think of him) was not a man to give up easily, I'll have to give him that. He switched to another line of argument quicker and slicker than one of those pips would zip through the tubing when you heated it up.

"Then think of your duty to humanity!" he urged me. "Think of all those little children deep in the heart of Texas or along the rockbound coast of Maine or the sunny shores of Hawaii. They will never know the joy—the pure wonder—of biting into one of your savory popapples—or whatever we choose to call them—unless we help you get the product out to them."

Now I have to admit that children are one of my weak spots, and the idea that more than ninety-nine per cent of them in these United States (to say nothing of the rest of the world) would be denied the experience of biting into a warm, juicy popapple—well, it did make me feel a mite regretful. Old Moneybags saw my weakness, and he pounced just like the cat when he got close enough to the bird.

"That's what we can do for you, Sir," he told me. "Between you and me and the conglomerate, we'll put smiles on the faces of every boy and girl in America! Why, with our mass-marketing skills and distribution network, we'll get the cost down to where everyone—not just the rich and famous—will be able to enjoy a sweet, juicy popapple whenever they want. Just think about that! Popapples for the masses!"

"Do you really think you could market that many?"

"Huh? Can Hershey do chocolate? Can Coca-Cola do soda pop? We can sell them pre-popped or put out the pips so that people can pop their own. Either way, we can have the whole country covered in a matter of months!"

"You might have a small problem selling them pre-popped," I said and then explained how quickly they seem to spoil if left uneaten.

"Not to worry there," he assured me. "Our chemical additives department will solve that little problem in no time."

"Whoa there!" I said. "Chemical additives in my popapples? I'm not sure if I go for that idea."

"Don't get yourself all upset over a little thing like additives. Ours are made with only the finest all-natural artificial ingredients. People will hardly notice them at all, and we're not putting very many in. Hey! The faster people have to eat these things, the faster they'll be buying more of them."

I was still wondering just what all-natural artificial ingredients might consist of, but before I could put that question to him, old Moneybags pulled out a checkbook and began writing one out.

"This is just to show you how serious we are," he said as he offered it to me. "All you have to do is agree to negotiate with us before you talk to anyone else."

I nodded and he handed it over. Then all of a sudden it sounded like a war had broken out right there inside the pavilion.

IX.

You see, Johnny, I should have realized that Abner Jenkins would not be attending the Greater Snodgrass County Fair all by himself. I believe I mentioned to you that Abner's light does not shine all that brightly. Well, that would be an understatement. Abner is one of these folks who spend their spare time sticking pins into electrical sockets and never seem to learn from the experience. The poor boy needs someone to look after him, and that was just what someone was *supposed* to be doing.

That someone was his brother Homer. Now Homer himself is not the brightest campfire on the hillside, but compared to Abner, he's a raging conflagration. Homer's main problem is that he's cursed with curiosity. He's forever taking things apart just to see how they work. This would be fine if he could put them back together again, but that's a talent that has so far eluded him.

Homer had left his brother just inside the pavilion while he wandered off to watch the pitchmen on the midway. Gadgets and gizmos and the hucksters who sold them would draw him like a magnet draws iron. I suppose he only meant to leave Abner alone for a few minutes while he checked things out. But by the time a salesman pitching an automatic salsa-maker caught Homer taking one of his models apart and ran him off, the better part of two hours had passed. In the meantime Abner had found himself a job as my assistant and pipapopper guardian.

Of course, when Homer saw *that* contraption, he was hooked. He had to know everything about that pipapopper and how it worked—and explaining things was not one of Abner's strong points. So Homer just naturally had to start tinkering with it.

I have to say that Abner apparently did try to discourage him, but no amount of reasoning could stop Homer once his attention was focused. He caught on to the basic idea fairly quickly (for him, that is), and nothing poor Abner might say could stop him from loading it up and giving it a try.

Now I suppose if he had used just one pip like I did, then the disaster that followed might have been prevented. I would have heard the explosion and hightailed it back there in time to stop things before they got completely out of hand. But Homer poured nearly half a jar of pips into the popping chamber all at once. Then, Johnny, he lit the burner.

X.

I had just accepted old Moneybags' check when *Bambambambambambam!* It sounded almost exactly like an automatic rifle, and for an instant I had a flashback to my younger days when I helped train one of the first companies of green berets. I was out of my chair and under the table before I even realized what I was doing.

I guess the first popapple actually did hit the net. But Homer had removed the clamps that held the contraption in place in order to get a better look at its inner workings, so the pipapopper began bucking, jumping and spinning as it fired. The result of this was that the next 283 pips (That's an estimate, but probably pretty close.) went every which way and spread chaos and general devastation across 32,750 square feet of a pavilion jammed full of food products, arts and crafts and all the people checking them out.

"Great galloping catfish!" I cried, as a popapple the size of a bowling ball shot past my nose and slammed into the table next to us, causing total carnage among two chicken-fried duck dinners with all the trimmings and a full bottle of Snodgrass County Pure Premium Wild Huckleberry Wine—the '97 vintage, no less!

Bam! Bam! Two more popapples took out the Greater Snodgrass County 4-H display. I think those kids were trying to show the benefits of raising early spring chickens on alfalfa sprouts or something along that line. It was hard to tell after those popapples passed through.

Next a display featuring twelve jars of Granny Peterson's prize-winning persimmon preserves went flying like a set of bowling pins hit in a perfect strike. And what three other popapples did to the Greater Snodgrass County Quilting Society's display—Johnny, I won't even attempt to describe that!

The miracle was that nobody was seriously hurt. Just about everyone, including me, went under the tables or flat on the floor with their hands over their heads and eyes closed like the Last Judgment was at hand. The one notable exception was Homer Jenkins.

Homer's one true talent is for self-preservation, I'll have to give him that. When he saw the results of his tinkering, he realized he would be *persona non grata* at the fair for a considerable time to come. So he did what he always did when he found himself in trouble—which tended to happen frequently. He lit out for the back country without bothering to offer explanations and left poor Abner to take the blame.

Mr. Moneybags also appeared to have had a change of heart. He left on a stretcher in the capable hands of the Greater Snodgrass County Fire & Rescue Department. He stood when he should have ducked and had caught a popapple square in the brisket. As they carried him away, he did manage to gasp out, "Don't call us. We'll call you."

After the firing stopped, Myer O'Dwyer stood up and dusted himself off. "Oy vey and begorra!" he muttered as he gazed at the devastation around him. "It looks like your invention still needs a little work."

"That does appear to be the case," I agreed as I looked at the havoc that Homer's tinkering had caused. I hadn't seen a mess like that since the tornado passed though the featherbed factory.

"Two questions, Grandpappy. Who is responsible and who is going to pay for everything?"

Well, the answers seemed obvious—but were they? Homer Jenkins was directly responsible, but he was already long gone. Abner was responsible for letting Homer play with the pipapopper, but could I honestly pin the blame on him? Nope. I was the one responsible for hiring Abner to mind the machine. So I was the one who was going to have to take the consequences.

Those consequences looked to be painfully expensive, but then I remembered the check from Dipoquet & Monebaggio. It was still safe in my wallet, so I hauled it out for a closer look—and gasped! Old Moneybags had dated and signed the check, *but he had left the amount for me to fill in!*

I quickly endorsed it over to the Greater Snodgrass County Fair and gave it to Myer O'Dwyer. "Fill it in for the amount the damage comes to," I told him. "But I suggest you deposit it quick-like before Moneybags has a change of heart." Myer already had his calculator out and was hard at work.

That solved one problem, but I still had to deal with Abner Jenkins. I found him cowering under the table where the wreckage of my pipapopper still lay smoking and smoldering. When I hauled him out, he had the most woeful and woebegone expression I have ever seen. Just imagine the look you might see on a puppy you've caught making a mess on your best carpet, and you'll get the picture.

"Grandpappy," he said real slow and solemn-like. "Does this mean I don't get no hot dogs?"

"Abner," I replied, "at this very moment my mind is working overtime trying to come up with the most horrible things I could do to you and that consarned brother of yours. But while I'm thinking about it, come on. I'll buy you a couple of hot dogs."

XI.

Now Johnny, you might think that the debacle at the fair and the check I had to sign over would put an end to the adventure of the popapples, but I'm afraid there was more bad news to come.

First, the awards committee got together and decided that the mess Homer Jenkins had created made me ineligible for any trophies, ribbons medals or cash. The *Snodgrass County Sentinel* even refused to print my name. It seems the editor was a bit miffed because he never got to taste a popapple. So old Orville Whatshisname wound up with all the glory once again.

The *Sentinel* did report on the mess the popapples had made and the stench they began to create a couple of hours later. While that did satisfy my curiosity on one point—just how long would they keep—the whole fair had to close down for the day while the pavilion was fumigated and the displays set back up. That made lots of people very upset and angry.

In fact, Sheriff Culpepper wanted to put a bounty on Homer Jenkins' head, but the County Board of Supervisors persuaded him to have Homer declared a public nuisance instead. So Homer officially became what I knew him to be all along.

As for me, I slipped out of the fairgrounds as quietly and inconspicuously as I could, which is not easily done when you're toting a ruined pipapopper under your arm, and made my way back to Ruination Farm. I was just counting my blessings, in the form of dollars I had acquired—in fact, I had just totaled the receipts—when the knock came at my door.

"Great galloping catfish! Now who could that be?" I wondered.

Well, this knock had some authority behind it. In fact, it was the kind of knock that seemed to say, "You had better respond right now, this very instant!" So I did. The knocker behind the knuckles turned out to be a government agent.

"Fiske. U.S.D.A.D.P.D.," he said in that clipped way government agents have of speaking, the kind that implies that you knew all along and were probably guilty of some terrible misdeed.

"Do tell!" I said wonderingly. "I take it Fiske is your name, but what do the other letters stand for?"

"United States Department of Agriculture, Dangerous Plants Division. I'm here to check your permit."

"What permit?" I asked.

"Your permit to grow, produce and sell a controlled substance," he informed me in his most official manner.

"Controlled substance? Are you accusing me of being a drug dealer?" Now I was getting riled and developing a bad case of the blue jimhickies at the same time. Neither of these is good for the old blood pressure.

"You are accused of endangering the general welfare of the American public by growing and selling an explosive substance. Do you have the proper warning labels?"

"What warning labels? I sell the pips already popped."

"Then let me see your popping permit."

"A permit to pop popapple pips? I don't believe there is such a thing."

"That is no excuse," he said as he began writing out a citation. "Since this is your first offense, we will let you off with a fine and a warning. But you are strictly forbidden to grow, produce or sell popapples without the proper popapple production and popping permit."

"And just where and how do I procure the proper popapple production and popping permit?" I wanted to know.

"You can't. They don't exist," he replied as he handed me the citation. "In fact, popapples themselves do not exist."

"The folk who ate them at the fair might argue that point," I reminded him. "They seemed to find them pretty tasty."

"The United States Government has never concerned itself with matters of taste," he answered, and I sure had to believe him on *that*. "Plow up your popapple plants, and we'll burn them at one of our ordinance disposal sites."

With that, he handed me the citation and I shuggered. That's a combination of a shrug and a shudder, and it can't be done under normal circumstances. But when you're faced with an awful situation that you can't escape, it becomes quite natural. That citation would wipe out all but a dollar and fifty cents of my fair profits. I didn't say anything, though, for fear that U.S.D.A.D.P.D. man would come up with a way to get that last buck and a half as well.

I understand the United States Army had quite a time of it when they burned all those plants. Of course the heat caused all the pips to pop, and the soldiers who had good hands got themselves an unexpected treat. Or maybe it wasn't so unexpected. I am told that, buried deep in the armed forces appropriations records, is a request for several dozen pounds of cinnamon and sugar to be sent to one particular ordinance disposal site.

Well, I hope those soldiers enjoyed themselves.

The government still sends a man out every now and then just to make sure I'm not growing any more popapples. But I promised them I wouldn't, and I'm a man who keeps his word—even if I do get a little careless with the truth every now and then.

But Johnny, I never promised I would get rid of *all* the pips. So if you were to come out to Ruination Farm around the Fourth of July, when small explosions don't cause that much concern, I might just fire up the old barbecue pit and—how good are you at catching things, anyhow?

Great Galloping Catfish!

I.

Johnny, I understand there is some argument about the river that runs past Ruination Farm. Is it called the W-*inn*-dy River or the W-*eye*-ndy River? Well, since it is both of these things, I guess you could call it whichever you want. That's what I do.

You can bet the wind blows pretty strong along the old Windy sometimes. When that stream has a good tailwind behind it, the current just zips along. The loggers who worked up in the Dismal Hills back in the old days would wait for a good following wind and then float their log rafts down to the mills so doggone quickly that those logs scarcely had time to get wet before they arrived.

But sometimes the wind would blow contrary, and then the river would slow down to where it just barely crept along. Johnny, I remember one year when, after four straight days of strong headwinds, the river just gave up and started back the way it came. Sure caused an awful mess back up at its headwaters.

Then there were the times when the wind blew slantwise across it. When that happened, the river would leave its bed and search for a new one—sort of like a sleepy man who can't quite get comfortable no matter what position he tries. Then the wind might die down to nothing, and the river would get all confused and not know what to do. So it would just lie there in its bed and not flow anywhere.

But that river also winds around more than any other stream in all of North America. I would bet, if you could somehow take that river and pull it out into a straight line, it would be longer than the Mississippi, the Missouri and the Columbia all put together. You could probably add in a few hundred miles of the Colorado for good measure.

A few miles upstream from Ruination Farm there's a place called Parker's Knot, where that river runs so crooked that it actually doubles back on itself and forms kind of a slip knot. Back during the big floods of '86, that river actually twisted itself around into the neatest clove hitch you ever did see.

But it was drought and not floods that caused my problem with the great galloping catfish. It was back in the early '90's when we went almost two years to the day without a drop of rain. Oh sure, we got some snow during the winter, but it was the driest snow you ever saw—no water content to it at all. I recall I went out once with a washtub, filled it with snow and packed it down good and tight. But when I set it on the stove to melt, all I got for my trouble was four little drops that evaporated before I could get the darn tub off the stove.

So you can imagine what that drought did to the river. Why, it dired up to where it was just pools and puddles here and there. All the fish were cut off and trapped, and I'm afraid almost all of them died. All but those great galloping catfish, that is.

Now they weren't gallopers to begin with, but that's what they became. One morning I happened to notice a couple of them using their fins like legs to sort of slide themselves along through the mud from one pool to the next. At first it was all they could do to scrabble-crawl for five ot ten yards. But pretty soon the better ones could make fifteen or twenty. Then it was thirty to forty. Then fifty, and then even more.

I soon realized I was witnessing a natural phenomenon. Those catfish were evolving right before my eyes—and doing a mighty quick job of it too! Of course, I suppose that survival is a pretty powerful incentive. Not only were their fins becoming more and more like legs, but their gills were getting to where they could do double duty as lungs. Or at least for short stretches they could.

Those catfish are becoming a brand-new sub-species, I realized one morning as I watched a bunch of them work their way from pool to pool. So I thought it was only right to give them a new name and classification all their very own.

The scientific folk classify this particular type of fish as *Siluriformes*. So I decided to give this particular variety the name of *Siluriformes grandpappyes*. Then I set about observing them in their new habitat.

Johnny, it was amazing how quickly they adapted. Those fins of theirs grew longer and stronger until they could scoot nearly a quarter mile along that dried-up old riverbed. I put a stopwatch on some of them, and the best got to where they could do the quarter-mile in ninety seconds flat. That may not be much by human standards, but it's a lot faster than your average fish can run.

Finally the rains came again, and the river filled its bed and began running in its same old cantankerous way. I was pretty sure that my *Siluriformes grandpappyes* would de-evolve back to their old form and habits. But there it seems I was wrong.

II.

I guess those catfish had taken a liking to that big old world beyond their riverbed. They couldn't stay topside very long during the heat of the day. Catfish don't have scales, you know, and I guess a bad case of sunburn would be goshawful uncomfortable to a fish. But at night they'd come up and skitter along the surface on those long, leglike fins they'd developed. And those lunglike gills got better and stronger too. Pretty soon they could stay up for several minutes at a stretch.

And that wasn't all they learned to do.

Have you ever listened to a catfish singing in the night? It's what I would call a unique experience, though it's hard to describe in precise terms. I suppose if you took the howl of a coyote and mixed it with the scream of a panther, then added the hoot of an owl and maybe included some fingernails scraping down a chalkboard—then you might get a rough idea of what I was treated to every night when the moon was full or nearly so. It sure didn't make for a restful evening.

But their singing soon became the least of my worries. During their forays onto dry land those catfish had broadened their diet to include an extensive sampling of my vegetable garden. In fact they tried a little bit of everything, even including a popapple—but only one catfish tried that, and, needless to say, he only tried it once.

Now I might have put up with a little vegetable pilfering now and then. Other critters besides me have to eat, after all. But it soon became obvious by the tracks they left that those catfish were growing bigger and bolder almost by the day. One morning I came out to find two of my best chickens missing and a trail of feathers leading down to the river.

Something was going to have to be done—and soon!

III.

That very morning, while I was going over possible solutions to my peculiar problem, I heard a knock at my door. It was a knock that had a very familiar rhythm to it.

"Great galloping catfish!" I cried. "Could it be? Is she back?"

The odds were pretty good, because old Hairball hissed, laid his ears back farther than any cat's ears have a right to go and then shot under the bed like he had been fired from my pipapopper. And when I opened the door, sure enough, there she was—the little old woman who brought me the apple that got me in all that trouble.

"You know," I said as I faced her in the doorway, "I'm a bit hesitant about inviting you in. Your last visit didn't work out very well for me."

"Ah!" she said with a toothless smile. "You shouldn't blame me for your own poor judgment. Letting the Jenkins brothers come within a mile of your popper and pips was pretty poor planning on your part.."

"It sure was," I admitted. "Now I've got the DEA, the FDA, the FTC, the FBI, the CIA and a bunch of other abbreviations I've never even heard of out here about every week checking to see if I'm growing something that I shouldn't. But how did you know about the Jenkins boys? I sure didn't see you out at the fair."

The old woman cackled and rubbed the tip of her nose with her lower lip. "It's my business to know other people's business," she replied.

"You mean to tell me you're a professional snoop? A snitch? An informer?" Johnny, I was shocked to think that my own government would hire some-one like that to spy on me. However, her reply shocked me even more.

"No. I don't work for your government. I'm a witch. A witch-in-exile, if you want to be technical. I'm also your neighbor. If you'll let me come in and rest my weary bones, and fix me just a little something to line my stomachs, I'll tell you all about myself."

Well, I thought, *if that ain't enough to curdle the carrots!*

It was against my better judgment, but we do have a code of hospitality here in Snodgrass County, even though we're stuck out several miles east of Elsewhere. So I told her to come on in and sit a spell while I rustled up some grub.

Now as a rule I don't ask personal questions of folks I don't know all that well, but something that old woman said struck me as rather odd. "I don't mean to be nosy," I said to her, "but did you just say *stomachs*—as in more than one?"

"Of course," she said. "I have three of them. One is for storing, one is for cooking and one for digesting. You mean you weren't aware of that?"

I had to confess my ignorance of the subject. "I'm afraid I don't know all that much about the inner workings of a witch's anatomy," I told her. "I don't know much about the outer workings either. In fact, I've never even met a witch before."

"Yes, I know. I pity you poor humans with only one stomach—not very efficient at all. But if you will be so kind as to get me a little something from your refrigerator, I'll demonstrate how mine work."

Johnny, I wasn't sure if I was ready for such a demonstration. But when a witch makes a request, it's a good idea to grant it. So I took out three eggs, a hunk of cheese, two strips of raw bacon, half a loaf of bread and a stick of butter. Then I piled them on a plate and set them in front of her. She opened her big old mouth and slid the whole mess right down her gullet. Then she frowned a bit pensively.

"There's a little something lacking," she concluded. "Would you happen to have an onion?" I handed her one the size of a tennis ball, and she didn't even bother to peel it. Instead she flipped it in the air, caught it in her mouth on its way down and swallowed it whole. Then she let loose a tremendous belch.

"Pardon me," she said. "That always happens when I start cooking." She blew a cloud of steam from her nose, and by golly! The whole room smelled like breakfast being prepared. I wasn't sure whether to feel delighted or disgusted.

"Three stomachs!" I marveled. "Just imagine!" I was a little miffed when I thought of all the work I had gone to the first time she visited. She probably could have done the job for me while she slept.

"A cow has four stomachs. So why shouldn't a witch have three?" she replied. And how could I argue with logic like that? I decided to change the subject instead.

"Look here," I said to her. "If we're neighbors, we should get to know each other. May I be so bold as to ask your name?"

"Certainly," she replied. "Down here in this dimension I like to go by Granny Grimoire." (She pronounced it Grem-*wahr*.) "Has a certain ring to it, don't you think?"

"Granny, could you please explain what you mean by *down here in this dimension*?"

"It's rather hard to put it in terms you would understand," she said. "I suppose the closest thing would be the idea of a parallel universe."

"Okay. I sort of understand that."

"Then let's just say that I should be there, but I'm here instead."

"But why? Do you prefer it down here?"

"Not at all! As I told you, I'm a witch-in-exile. I did something that would correspond to breaking one of your rules or laws or whatever you call them. So I was banished down here for a certain length of what you call time."

"How much of it?" I asked.

"Just a hundred of your years. But there was one other little catch."

"There always is," I observed.

"Indeed. I have to do something nice for someone down here. It's actually a bit more complicated, but that's the easiest way of putting it." She sighed and belched again. "Excuse me. That's my timer going off. I don't want to burn the bacon."

She sighed again and I heard a series of odd rumblings from her midsection. Something strange was going on down there, but I decided I would be a gentleman and pretend not to notice.

"I'm afraid I made a mess of things, Grandpappy," she said after some thought. "Do you mind if I call you that? Everyone else seems to."

"Not at all," I assured her. "But what do you mean by making a mess of things? If you're thinking about those popapples, that was probably more my fault than yours."

"Well, they were part of it."

Part of it? That set me to thinking. "Granny, did you have something to do with those talking snakes?"

"Yes," she admitted. "The poor things seemed so abused and picked on. I wanted them to experience life at a higher level, and speech seemed one way to do it."

"And what about that old white crow?"

"Oh yes, him too. He was always such a mean one. I decided to see if changing his plumage would improve his disposition, but I'm afraid it only made him worse."

"Granny, it's just not a good idea to fool around with nature."

"Don't you think nature could use a little improving sometimes?" she answered me. "Didn't you change this land into a farm?"

"Yes I did. But Granny, that's vegetation. We don't much go for altering animal species. Natural selection works best. Survival of the fittest, we call it." You see, Johnny, I was trying to be diplomatic. You don't want to get arbitrary and bossy with a witch—not even a witch-in-exile. No telling what she might do then.

Granny Grimoire just smiled at that. "Oh?" she said. "You don't breed animals? You don't clone animals?" I have to admit she had me there.

"Where I come from," she continued, "we practice *un*natural selection and survival of the most interesting. It makes life a lot more exciting."

"I imagine it does. But Granny, you're not there. You're *here*. That being the case, you really ought to play by our rules."

"Oh all right," she agreed. "But that's going to make it a lot more difficult to deal with those catfish."

"Granny, are you responsible for them as well?"

"I'm afraid so. The poor things were suffering so much from that drought. I thought that if they had an alternate means of getting from place to place, they would survive. And they did!" she added triumphantly.

"But Granny, consider the cost! They're starting to multiply faster than a calculator on methamphetamine! They've already wiped out all the other fish from here up to Parker's Knot, and the Good Lord only knows how far downstream they've spread. And now they're starting to come out on dry land! Granny, just what are we going to do with them?"

"I think you need to round them up," she said.

"Granny, that's easy to say, but it's not quite so easy to do. Just how would you suggest I go about rounding up a cluster of catfish?"

"Well, what do your cowboys use to round up cattle?"

"Horses, of course. But Granny, a horse isn't going to be of much use in a river."

"A *land* horse wouldn't," she agreed. "But a river horse would."

"Granny! There ain't no such animal! Not in this dimension, anyway."

"Oh yes there is!" she informed me. "You have them right here on your planet, though not in this particular corner of it. I believe you call them hippopotamuses or hippopotami."

"A hippo? Granny, I could never ride a hippo! They're huge! They're clumsy! And as I recall, they've got a pretty mean disposition!"

The old woman just laughed and belched again. "There's still some bread down there, and I'd like to toast it," she said. "Do you have any jam?"

I handed her a jar of strawberry preserves and a tablespoon. She swallowed three spoonfuls, burped again, and the room was full of the scent of toast and preserves.

"You still haven't answered my question," I reminded her. "How do I round up catfish with a hippopotamus?" (Johnny, in the whole history of the human race, I'll bet that question has never been asked before. It's certainly never been answered.)

"How many kinds of land horses do you have?" she asked.

"Oh, probably dozens. There's thoroughbreds, quarter horses, mustangs, clydesdales, shetlands, apaloosas..." I rattled off a few more, and she just smiled and nodded at me.

"Exactly! Well, in my dimension we breed river horses the same way you breed land horses. I can get you just the kind you need to round up those pesky catfish."

Well, I was tempted, no question about that. But I also remembered the trouble those popapples had caused and the mess and bother I had with those snakes and their model airplanes. Would I be able to handle a modified hippopotamus? I told Granny I would think on it overnight and give her my answer in the morning.

That night I was treated to another catfish concert, and when I set out to do the morning chores, I found another chicken missing. Furthermore, old Hairball was cowering up in the sycamore tree. There were finprints in the dirt at the base of the tree showing where the catfish had looked up at him while they howled. It took me an hour to coax him back down, and I had to put him on tranquilizers for a week.

"It's a good thing those catfish can't climb trees," I told him as I stroked his fur and hand-fed him a few kitty-nibbles I'd laced with some mild sedatives. But then another disturbing thought occurred to me. *They can't climb trees yet!* But how long would it be before they could shinny right up that sycamore after him? That was what decided me.

"Granny, it looks like drastic measures must be taken," I told her when she came by later that morning. "So bring me your doggone hippopotamus!"

IV.

Granny came back that afternoon leading the oddest, strangest, just plain flat-out *weirdest*-looking critter I have ever seen. Now it did look just a bit like a hippo. It had the head of one, that's for sure, and its feet were big and round like a hippo's. But the body was all slimmed down like it had spent six years in weight-watchers. Furthermore, it had the long neck of a horse and stood only fifteen or sixteen hands high, which is about the size of your regular horse. Its legs were slim and well-muscled, but those huge round feet made it look like a horse that had stuck each hoof in a bucket of cement. Its color was gray all over, and it had just a little stub of a tail.

"Great galloping catfish, Granny!" I cried. "Do you expect me to ride that thing?"

"Of course," she said. "You've ridden land horses, haven't you?"

"Many's the time," I replied as I took a closer look at the beast. Once you got past its strange appearance, it did look like it could be ridden. "But I don't have any tack for it. I hope you don't expect me to ride bareback. I'm getting just a bit old for that."

"Certainly not. I have everything you'll need right here."

She handed me a large sack she had brought along, and I took out a saddle and saddle blanket. The hippo stood calmly grazing on some timothy hay while I put them on. Then, instead of a bridle, she took out two long strips of leather, each with a loop at one end.

"Open, Hippo!" she commanded, and the weird hippopotamus obediently open its huge mouth. She deftly slipped the loops over each of its lower tusks. "Use these just like you would use the reins on a horse," she said. "You may have to pull just a bit harder, but the idea is the same."

I guess I should have felt honored, being the first person (in this dimension, at least) ever to ride a hippopotamus—or at least this particular breed of hippo. But, Johnny, I must confess I felt a little nervous as I swung myself into the saddle and waited to see what would happen. Would the critter buck? It's been many a year since I rode bucking broncs on the rodeo circuit, and my skills in that particular area had grown a trifle rusty.

But that old hippo didn't move a muscle. It just stood there awaiting orders like the most docile plug you could imagine. So I gave it a slight nudge with my knees, and it set off around the pasture like it wanted to show me what a gentle creature it would be. I noticed it was a pacer, not a trotter. That is, it moved its left forefoot and hind foot together. A trotter, of course, moves the left forefoot and right hind foot together.

"That's its land gait," Granny explained when I mentioned this fact to her as we passed by. "On water it trots."

Well, *that* was news to me! I knew that hippopotami felt right at home in the water as swimmers and floaters, and I could tell this parallel hippo was a lot lighter than our earthly variety. But light enough to trot on the water? I had my doubts.

"You'll have to put on its water shoes before it can go out on the river," Granny explained as I dismounted after two laps around the pasture.

"*Water shoes?* Granny, I've never heard of any such things!"

"Well, you've heard of snow shoes, haven't you?"

"I have indeed," I told her. "Matter of fact, I wore them many a time back when I was a miner up in the High Sierras."

"Well, it's the same principle," she assured me. "They just slip on right over his feet. Let's take him down to the river, and I'll show you how they work."

So we led that slimmed-down hippo to the riverbank where Granny had stashed another big sack. She pulled out a contraption that looked like a cross between a pontoon and a buoy. "You don't want to have him wear these on land," she warned me. "Too easy to get a puncture."

I was wondering how she was going to get them on, but that hippo apparently had been trained and knew just what to do. It lifted each foot in turn and kept it up until Granny had slipped on the water shoe and tightened the cinch that ran around the top. When she finished, that hippo stood a good two to three hands higher than before, and it took a little effort to get back into the saddle.

"Now take it easy until you get the feel of it," she warned as the hippo stepped out onto the river. She needn't have worried though. I was a pretty fair jockey back in my younger days—though modesty compels me to add that I grew too heavy before I got the chance to ride in any of the big races. I figured that if I could handle a skittish colt, then I surely ought to be able to ride a docile river horse.

I kept him at a gentle walk until he got the feel of the river and the sense of the current and where and how fast it flowed. We went upstream a ways and then back downstream, and when I felt he was comfortable with the river and with me, I stepped him up to a jog trot. We went upstream a quarter-mile in that fashion, and then I turned him and brought him back down at a full, hard reaching trot—almost a canter, in fact.

After half a mile, I figured he was warmed up enough, so I turned him again, gave the reins a shake, stood up in the stirrups and cried, "Come on, Hippo! Turn it loose!"

Johnny, you don't know what a thrill is until you've galloped over the surface of a river on the back of a hippopotamus! We fairly tore along the old Windy, with the water spattering behind us. I couldn't help myself. I waved my hat and yelled, *"Yee-hah!"* like I hadn't yelled in years. It was just plain downright exhilarating!

But thrilling and exiting as it was, galloping Old Hippo up and down the Windy River didn't really solve my problem. How was I going to deal with those pesky galloping catfish? I was just heading back for shore, scratching my head in a puzzled sort of way, when the answer came to me. I could treat those galloping catfish just like stray dogies out on the range. Yes sir, indeed I could!

I think I mentioned that I once rode bucking broncs on the rodeo circuit, but my greatest love was calf roping. I was pretty sure my old lariat was still up in my attic somewhere. *(Dang! I'm going to have to clean that place out someday!)* Well, it took me a while, but I found it—a little dusty, but still in good enough shape to do the job.

"Catfish," I said as I coiled it up and started back down the ladder, "you are about to get the biggest surprise of your lives. And for at least one of you, it's going to be the *final* surprise!"

V.

I figured it was best to leave old Hippo tethered in the trees down by the river until after sunset. There was no telling when some inspector from the Department of This, That or Whatever might come snooping around to see if I was growing something they disapproved of. That young fellow Fiske from the USDADPD was the most eager of the bunch, but there were some others close behind him. Anyway, the catfish wouldn't come up until the moon was high, and by then the snoops would be safely home in bed.

So I retired early and didn't bother to set the alarm. I knew the catfish would take care of that for me. Sure enough, it was just a mite after eleven when I heard them begin to howl. I rolled out of bed, got back into my clothes, stopped long enough to reassure old Hairball—whom I kept inside, just in case—and then headed down to the river.

Hippo was waiting for me, and I could tell he was ready by the way he pawed the ground and—well, he didn't actually whinny. I guess it was more like a rumble, but it was enough to satisfy me that he was eager to do business. Even so, I had some reservations. A good cow pony is a highly-trained specialist, and I wasn't sure if Hippo's background suited him for this particular job. Well, I calculated there was just one way to find out.

I quickly got him saddled, slipped the loops over his tusks and the put on his water shoes. Then I climbed into the saddle, shook out a loop in my lasso, gave that old hippopotamus a nudge with my knees and called out, "Come on, Hippo! Let's get 'em, Big Fella!"

Hippo's rumble rose to a sound that was about halfway between a snort and a growl as he charged out onto the river. Those catfish stopped their howling pronto and began galloping downstream on those leglike fins they'd been evolving. I thought, *why don't they dive?* After all, it would be easy to escape us below the surface.

It took a few seconds to figure it out, but I came to the conclusion that their gills had halfway evolved into lungs, and they didn't yet have a way of switching quickly from one form of breathing to another.

Old Hippo quickly erased any doubts I might have had about his ability to control those catfish and cut an individual out from the herd. Just a nudge with a knee and a gentle tug on a rein was enough. I'd picked out a nice big plump one, and Hippo had him separated from the rest and skittering across the water on his own before he could even realize he was in big, big trouble.

By that time I was twirling the lasso over my head, timing that catfish's little skitter-jumps and getting set to cast. "Hippo," I said to my steed, "I hope you know the rest of the routine!" Then I slung the rope, and the noose dropped over the catfish's head right in mid-jump. Johnny, it was just like the old days back in the rodeo arena!

A good roping horse, when he sees that the cowboy has made a successful throw, will hit the brakes so hard that he dang-near sits down right on his backside. And that is just what old Hippo did! That rope went taut as a bowstring, and that great galloping catfish came to a very sudden stop in mid-jump. Then it flopped right onto the water on its back. I was halfway out of the saddle after it before I realized this wasn't a calf in the arena, that I didn't have any water shoes and that a good soaking would be the least of my worries if I continued.

So I turned old Hippo for the bank and snaked that catfish out onto dry land, where I finished it off with a couple of whacks from my trusty seven-iron. I'd just got it filleted and ready to tote back to my freezer, when who should appear but Granny Grimoire. How she got across the river—I don't know. But here she was.

"They're best eaten fresh," she said, "and I have a little campfire going over yonder. Why don't we fix ourselves a little midnight supper?"

Johnny, when a witch—even a witch-in-exile—extends an invitation, it's a good idea to go along with it. Granny had a nice little campfire going, a frying pan that was just the right size and some butter and breading already prepared. I took off old Hippo's saddle and turned him loose to graze while Granny fried the fish.

"I know you have to eat it the old-fashioned way," she said as she handed me a plate, knife and fork. "It's not very efficient, but I suppose you have to do what you have to do." And with that, Johnny, she stuck her bare hand into that hot pan, took out her share, opened her mouth wider than any mouth has a right to open and dropped half a catfish right down her gullet. The belch she then gave nearly put out the campfire!

"Aah!" she said. "This is going to taste wonderful!"

"*Going* to taste? Granny, you've already swallowed it!"

"Of course. You see, we have our taste buds down in our stomachs. That way, we can use our tongues for talking and enjoy dinner at the same time. It's much more practical than your way of doing things."

I suppose she might have a point, but I was content to keep my taste buds right where they were. Seemed kind of unnatural to have them anywhere else, but of course Granny Grimoire was an unnatural being. So maybe the unnatural was perfectly natural to her.

But Johnny, I had forgotten over the years just how wonderful a late-night supper could be when it's cooked over a campfire out on a riverbank by moonlight. Granted, the old Windy doesn't cast quite the same spell as the Pecos or the Cimarron or even the Picketwire, and catfish isn't your usual cowboy fare. But it sure brought back the old memories, and if I'd had my guitar with me, I would have favored Granny with an old cowboy ballad or two from the days when I sang with the Sons of the Pioneers—though modesty compels me to add that I was only one of the backup singers.

VI.

This became almost a nightly event. By day I would keep old Hippo in the barn or tethered in the trees down by the riverbank. He seemed to know it would not be wise for anyone other than Granny or me to see him. He became very good at keeping out of sight and not calling attention to himself. I was developing a real warm spot in my heart for that old Hippo—just like the kind a cowboy has for his favorite horse.

A couple hours after sundown I'd hear him start to paw the ground and snort. He could sense when those catfish were getting set to come up. I'd get him saddled and ready, and we'd wait together in the trees. Pretty soon I'd spot a catfish poking its head out of the water, probably checking to see if the coast was clear. That was when I had to keep old Hippo absolutely still. If we moved too soon, that lookout would spot us and warn the others to stay down on the bottom.

But I reckon catfish have short memories and small brains. Pretty soon another head would pop up, then two or three more at a time, until a couple dozen of them were frolicking around on the surface of the old Windy.

Now if they'd been willing to stay out on the river, which was their natural habitat, then I would have been willing to let them be. But pretty soon they'd group together and start heading for shore, and I knew they were aiming to cause me some trouble.

"Steady there, Hippo!" I'd warn as they approached. See, I wanted them to get close to the shore, but not actually onto the riverbank. It's not sporting to chase a catfish down on dry land, after all—be sort of like shooting them in a barrel. Besides, I was getting downright fond of these nightly gallops up and down the river.

When they got within ten or twenty feet of the bank, I'd give old Hippo a nudge and we'd burst from cover and charge onto the river before those catfish could realize they had a serious problem. They'd scatter every which way, and I'd pick out a nice big plump one and have old Hippo after him before you could shout, "Benjamin Harrison!"

(No, Johnny. I don't know why you would want to shout, "Benjamin Harrison!" But it doesn't matter. You wouldn't have had time.)

By the time I had that catfish roped, snaked out onto the bank and dispatched, I'd see the light from Granny's campfire and know that supper would soon be ready. Johnny, you haven't lived properly until you've eaten catfish fried over an open camp-fire by moonlight! Even to this day my stomach just glows with yearning at the memory of it.

Of course we talked while we ate. Granny did most of that, since she had her mouth free at all times and I didn't. She'd tell me tales about her parallel universe, and I have to admit that most of it went clear over my head.

But one night she said to me, "Grandpappy, I'll be going back pretty soon. Would you like to come along and see my world firsthand?"

"Granny," I replied, "that's probably the greatest honor you could offer me, but my answer has to be no. I do plan to leave this world when the Good Lord tells me to, but I wouldn't do it for anyone else—no matter how nice they were."

"I kind of thought that's what your answer would be," she said rather sadly, and we let the matter drop and never brought it up again.

But I don't want you to think that Granny Grimoire and I had anything more than a just-good-friends relationship. She was my neighbor and I felt honored to count her as a friend, but she was defi-nitely *not* what you would call attractive. In fact, if she had entered the annual Greater Snodgrass County Ugly Person Contest (used to be the ugly *man* contest, but the politically correct folks said we had to open it to all comers), all the other entrants would have given up on the spot and gone home and told themselves how beautiful they were.

Besides, I had another problem on my mind just then.

VII.

You see, not all those nightly hunts were successful. When the moon was right at its fullest, those catfish would get careless to the point of being a little crazy. They'd pop up dozens at a time, and I might be able to rope three or four in one evening. Granny and I would fix one for supper, and I'd fillet the others to tote back to my freezer.

But when the moon was on the wane, those critters would grow a lot more careful and cautious. Instead of a hundred or more, there'd be only eight or ten of them come up, and maybe only two or three would make for the bank, where I had an excuse to take them. And on the nights when there was no moon, not a single catfish would show itself.

I figured those varmints were breeding faster than old Hippo and I could take them out. Besides, all those late nights were taking a toll on my constitution. It seems I was no longer as young as I was in the old days when I worked as a trail hand.

So it was a great relief to me when the answer showed up at my front door one morning. The answer came in the form of my friend Myer O'Dwyer, who was, among other things, Chairman of the Greater Snodgrass County Chamber of Commerce. "*Oy vey*, Grandpappy me bucko!" he said when I invited him in. "We've got ourselves a bit of a problem, and it's hopin' I am already that you can help us out."

"Do tell!" I responded politely. "What seems to be the trouble, Myer?"

"You know that our big charity fund-raiser is coming up in a couple of days, don't you?" he said with a worried frown.

"Indeed I do, and I'm planning to come."

"Well, the highlight is going to be a big fish-fry, and we've ordered a full shipment of frozen fish from one of those giant wholesale distributors. But they got their shipping labels all mixed up! We've just got six dozen cartons of ink-jet printer cartridges instead, and our frozen fish wound up at the University of Southern New Mexico—where they promptly thawed and spoiled before the mistake was discovered!"

"I do declare!" I said sympathetically.

"Grandpappy, that fish-fry is scheduled for three days from now, and we don't have a single fish to our name! Sure and we might catch a few between now and then, but the Old Windy is pretty well fished out, and we need at least a couple hundred! I was just hoping against hope you might come up with an idea."

Johnny, isn't it a wonderful thing when two problems come together and create their own solution? The Greater Snodgrass County Chamber of Commerce was suffering from a shortage of fish, and I was suffering from a surplus. All we needed was a way to turn my problem into their solution.

"Would catfish do?" I asked Myer.

"*Vey* and for sure!" he answered. "That's what we wanted to order, but they were so expensive that we had to go with other kinds instead."

"Myer," I said to him. "I just might be able to help you."

But even as I reassured him, I realized I had some problems to deal with. Myer O'Dwyer needed a whole bunch of catfish, and I had a whole bunch I wished to be rid of. So far, so good. The moon would be at its fullest tomorrow night—even better. But Myer's fish fry would be clear up around Somewhere Else, which was more than a dozen miles away. How do I round up all those fish and get them from Point A to Point B?

Driving them on the river would not be good. After half a mile or so they'd be ready to dive again and probably would. Besides, we'd have to go upstream through Parker's Knot, and the currents there are the most tricky and treacherous you will find on the whole North American Continent.

Nope, It would have to be a land drive. I would have to herd those catfish just like the cowboys did with their cattle along the Old Chisholm Trail. But we weren't blessed with a Chisholm Trail out in Snodgrass County, and I sure didn't want to drive those catfish along a major highway, even late at night. At least a few cars would pass us by, and the sight of a drover on a modified hippopotamus herding a cluster of catfish might tend to disrupt concentration and cause an accident.

Then I remembered the Old Stage Road.

That one is a bit before your time, Johnny, but it used to wind through the county connecting all the little towns. Nowadays we have freeways and bypasses, so I doubt if more than two or three cars a week drive the Old Stage Road for any great distance. At night we would probably have it all to ourselves.

So I asked Myer, "Can you meet me at Milepost 28 on the Old Stage Road at one o'clock sharp two nights from now and not breathe a word to anyone about what you see?"

"You're up to something, aren't you," he said with a worried frown. "This won't turn out like that caper with the popapples, will it?"

"I most certainly hope not," I said. "But if you can keep the rendezvous at Milepost 28, I think I can supply you with all the catfish you will need."

VIII.

I wanted that extra night to lull those catfish into a false sense of security. So I kept old Hairball in the house and secured the chicken coop as best I could. My garden was already pretty well picked over, so I wouldn't lose much by letting them have a free run at it. Besides, if all went according to plan, it would be their last run.

That night those great galloping catfish had themselves quite a time out at Ruination Farm, while Hippo and I just watched. Granny Grimoire didn't come over, but I figured she knew what was planned and would show up the next night. I hoped so. An extra hand on a drive was always welcome.

Sure enough, she showed up right at eleven on the following night, just like she'd had it on her calendar for weeks. "What would you like me to do, Grandpappy?" she asked.

"Well, Hippo and I can handle the main herd. Could you follow along in my wagon and collect any strays that might fall behind?"

"I think I could manage that," she said.

See, drovers usually work from behind a herd, but my plan was to have Hippo and me moving ahead of them. I'd been down to the feed store that morning and bought myself a big sack of shelled corn. Catfish—at least *these* catfish—seemed to fancy corn over just about any other vegetable. I figured if I left a little trail of corn behind me, those galloping catfish would follow me all the way to tarnation and back!

Just a bit before midnight the first catfish popped its head up and had a look around. It wasn't but a moment before there were two, then four, then a dozen, then a hundred—about then I stopped counting. They frittered and skittered around the surface for a few minutes while Granny, Hippo and I held our peace and waited. Then one big fella—he seemed to be the leader—headed for the bank, and all the rest followed him.

"Mark that big one, Granny," I said. "He'll be the one to watch."

You see, cattle on a drive always had a lead bull they would follow. I was hoping catfish might be the same, and it looked like I was right.

When they were all out on the bank and making for what was left of my garden, I eased old Hippo around behind them and got between those catfish and the river. Then I moved up on them real slow and easy-like. Just as they became aware of me and were fixing to bolt, I stopped, took a handful of shelled corn and threw it on the ground just ahead of them.

For a few seconds it was touch and go. Would they stop and feed or would they scatter? Then that big fella seemed to make up his mind. He skittered over to that corn and began to guzzle, and all the others followed him.

Hippo and I moved around them as they fed, and by the time they'd cleaned up that corn, we were fifty yards closer to the Old Stage Road—and fifty yards farther from the river. I gave a whistle to attract their attention, dropped some more corn and waited for them to come to it—which they did, and mighty quick-like too.

By this time Granny had eased in behind them with the straggler wagon. Actually it was my old buggy with my old plug horse who never moved faster than a shambling walk, but who could shamble right through a tornado and not think anything of it. We'd loaded on a big tub of water to save any stragglers who might run out of lung-power before we reached Milepost 28.

It was the easiest trail drive I've ever been on. All I had to do was scatter some corn every hundred yards or so, and all those catfish would scramble to get to it. See, I'd been observing them over the past few weeks, and I noticed how greedy they would get when it came to food. I was counting on this greed overcoming their natural sense of caution, and was I ever right on that account! Why, it was almost *too* easy!

Johnny, you can't say you've really lived until you've herded catfish by moonlight along an old country road. It brought back memories of the old days when I was a drover, so much so in fact that I

took one of our old trail songs, put some new lyrics to it and sang it there under the stars as we moseyed along. This is how it went.

> *"It's late in the evenin' when we round up the catfish,*
> *And then head 'em out in the dead of the night.*
> *Keep 'em a-movin', both the lean and the fat fish*
> *To make that ol' milepost before the first light.*
> *Whoopee ti-yi-yo! Get along, all you catfish!*
> *Don't try to scatter or wander or run.*
> *Whoopee ti-yi-yo! Get along all you catfish!*
> *You know by tomorrow you'll all be well-done!"*

All right, maybe it wasn't such a good idea to be singing like that if I didn't want to call attention to myself. But when there's a big, full moon above your head and a steady, sure-footed hippopotamus under your saddle (and how man cowboys could ever boast of *that*, I wonder), well, a man can't really be blamed for bursting into song.

Anyhow, just one person (aside from Myer O'Dwyer) witnessed the great catfish drive, and happened to be old By-and-By Jones, the county's most notorious drunk. (He was called that because he always said he was going to quit by and by.) Jones was on his way home after a night of excessive celebration. But when he saw me on old Hippo, herding a cluster of catfish and singing to them (and don't forget to add in the sight of an extremely ugly witch-in-exile trailing after us in a buggy), he threw down the bottle, ran all the way back to town, signed the pledge down at the Freewill Baptist Church the next morning and never touched a drop after that. So I guess we did a little extra good deed that night.

When we reached Milepost 28 an hour or so later, I sure had some mighty tired catfish on my hands. I didn't have to worry about them trying to scatter and run by then. They were so pooped and full of shelled corn that they could barely inch their way along. It's a good thing we hadn't tried for Milepost 29. They never would have made it that far.

Myer was waiting in his truck, and I'll admit his jaw dropped a ways at the sight of us. "Oy vey and begorra!" he cried. "I don't know how you did it, and I won't even ask. But you've brought us all the fish we'll ever need. How much do we owe you?"

"There's no charge, Myer. I'm glad to be rid of them," I said as we commenced slinging those catfish into the back of his truck. I counted 316 that we loaded, and Granny added 14 stragglers she'd picked up along the way.

"Well, at least stop by tomorrow. We'll treat the both of you to dinner."

Granny politely declined, and I could see the relief on Myer's face when she did. My own face must have glowed, because I was sure I'd seen the last of those pesky catfish.

But there, as it turned out, I was wrong.

IX.

"Grandpappy," Granny said as we slowly trotted home. "I've got a teeny little confession to make."

"What's that?" I asked warily. I could feel my sense of relief starting to evaporate like the morning dew on a hot day.

"I didn't give Mr. O'Dwyer all the stragglers I picked up. I held one back."

"Why would you want to do that?" I asked, a little peevishly this time. "The whole idea was to get rid of the consarned varmints!"

"But this little fella was so small that he wouldn't have made good eating. Besides, he was such a cute little thing, trying so hard to keep up with the others on his stubby little fins and never getting any corn because the bigger fish would just push him aside. Well, I guess you could say I felt sorry for him."

Now the idea of a witch, even a witch-in-exile, feeling sorry for anyone or anything startled me a bit. But then I realized it all fit into a pattern. Granny had felt sorry for those catfish during the drought, messed around with nature and created the problem we had (hopefully) just gotten rid of. She's felt sorry for that old white crow and tried to improve its disposition by changing its plumage. She'd felt sorry for Arnold Bennett, given him a voice, and thus started a miniature war.

As far as that goes, she may have felt sorry for me when she gave me those unnatural popapples and got me into trouble with state and federal agencies I'd never even heard of before. So is it any wonder that I felt a mite uncomfortable when she said she felt sorry for yet another critter?

"I thought I'd let you keep him as a pet," she explained. "He really is awfully cute—for a catfish, that is."

I took a look at him—at least I assume it was a him—and yeah, he was kind of cute in an ugly sort of way. But I had doubts about keeping him as a pet.

"What do you expect me to do with him?" I protested. A pet catfish just didn't appeal to me, not after what I'd been through with his pesky relations. I was all for dumping him back in the river, preferably clear up above Parker's Knot, and letting him take his chances. But Granny wouldn't hear of it and reminded me rather forcefully how she had loaned me old Hippo and helped with the drive.

"All right! I'll take the little varmint if you'll give me that tub to use as a pen. But I'm not responsible for what Hairball might do, and I'm sure not going to baby sit him."

"Oh, don't worry about that. He'll grow on you," Granny said, and I wasn't quite sure just how she meant that.

X.

Hairball reacted just about the way I expected. He hissed and snarled and then slunk under the bed for a couple of days. I saw him only when he came out to eat, which he did rather frequently. He was an ornery, paranoid cat, but he wasn't stupid.

I put the tub out by the barn and set a little canopy over it as a sunscreen during the heat of the day. "Now look here," I told that fish. "I'm doing this under protest. You're alive right now because I owe Granny a favor. But Ruination Farm is not the Ritz Hotel. You understand that?"

That little catfish popped his head out of the water, and I could just about swear I saw him nod. I have to admit that gesture softened me up a little.

"All right," I conceded. "I've got a little shelled corn left over, and I'll give you a bit each morning until it runs out. But I'm not going to be feeding you forever! And if you want to get out and roam at night, you do it at your own risk. Is that understood?"

Again that catfish popped his head out of the water and nodded.

"Guess I ought to give you a name if you're going to be living here," I concluded. "What do you think I should call you?" Never having named a catfish before, I was sort of at a loss for words. Then I remembered the name of the species—*Siluriformes*. That was a pretty long name for a pretty small fish, but perhaps if I shortened it a bit...

"How about Sil?" I asked, and that little catfish nodded again.

So, Johnny, that was how I got myself a pet catfish. He didn't seem to hold it against me that I had some of his relations in my freezer. At first he kept to his tub during the day. But as soon as the sun went down, he'd hop out, skitter around the farm and make a general nuisance of himself.

One evening he must have done something that really exasperated me, because I picked up a little stick and tossed it his way. Of course I took care to miss, since I didn't want to hurt him, after all. Well, the stick sailed past his head, and doggone if that little critter didn't skitter after it, scoop it up in his mouth and fetch it right back to me.

"Well now, if that ain't enough to curdle the ketchup!" I said to myself. So I gave the stick another toss, and he brought it back again. We wound up playing fetch for almost half an hour. By the time it got too dark to continue, little Sil had got so good that he could leap in the air and catch the stick in his mouth!

I gave him an extra helping of corn that night and added a few grubs and worms for protein. And as I made my way back to the house, I began to wonder what other kinds of tricks I might teach him.

It only took a week to get the basics down. Within a few days he had picked up on sit, stay, come, roll over and sit up. That last one was hard to do, since his hind fins weren't all that strong yet. He was *really* good at playing dead, though. He'd just flop once or twice, go stiff as a board and then, believe it or not, he'd start to stink, just like a real dead fish. I soon decided not to try that game anymore.

But fetch always remained his favorite, and he would have played that game by the hour if I could have spared the time. You might wonder, *by the hour?* Yep. That was indeed the case. Every day that catfish grew a little bigger and a little stronger. I guess that diet of shelled corn and hand-dug worms appealed to him.

Pretty soon he was out of his tub for three, four and then five hours at a stretch, and he took to following me around while I did the chores. On the really bright days I had to rub sunblock on him before I let him out of the tub. And would you believe it? Little Sil started developing a tan—just like those California beach folks!

One day he followed me right into the house, skittered over to Hairball's dish and helped himself to a sample of Hairball's kitty food. Of course the cat went ballistic, but there wasn't all that much he could do about it. By that time little Sil wasn't all that little. He just gave the cat a grin that seemed to ask, *"Just what do you plan to do about it, huh?"* Old Hairball went into a snit that lasted three days.

Naturally, I gave Sil a pretty strong lecture about respecting the property and privacy of other critters, and bless me, Johnny! I believe that catfish understood every word I spoke to him! He sort of hung his head—you might not think a catfish could do that, but this one did—and appeared, well, I guess you could say—contrite.

When I said, "Now are you going to promise me never to touch Hairball's food again?" he not only nodded, but answered with a little *yip* as well.

It was then I began to wonder if I could teach him how to speak.

XI.

I guess you could say I was successful, but only marginally so. Sil got the five vowels down, but he could never master the consonants. Thus his vocabulary consisted of combinations of *yip, yap, yep, yop* and *yup*. If he was really excited, he might come out with a *yipe!* as well.

I soon figured out that *yap yup!* translated as, "I'm hungry! Feed me!" (I heard that one several times a day.) On the other hand *yip yop!* was, "Let's play fetch!" (That one was pretty common too.) I guess that *yep yip* was, "My tub needs fresh water." But he saved his favorite for late in the evening. *Yip yipe* meant, "Grandpappy, let's go riding!"

You see, I was still keeping old Hippo down by the riverbank, and just like any land horse, he needed to be exercised some each day. So every evening, as soon as it was dark and those government snoops were off doing whatever it is government snoops do at night, I'd saddle him up, put on his water shoes and we'd have ourselves a rare old gallop out on the Windy River.

I was keeping a close watch to see if any other galloping catfish were still around and maybe in a mood to cause some mischief. So far I hadn't spotted a one. But the moon was on the wane, so that didn't mean much. I figured I'd best keep watch through the whole lunar cycle before I concluded that the crisis had passed.

Well, one night Sil followed me down to the river bank, and when he saw me mount old Hippo, he commenced to yip like his poor little heart was breaking.

"Do you mean to tell me you want to ride along?" I asked.

"*Yip-yipe-yip-yipe-yip!*" he answered, and I figured that meant, "Yes!"

So I made room for him behind me on the saddle—it was a hippopotamus saddle, after all, so there was plenty of extra room—and we trotted out onto the river together. It was a perfectly clear night, with just a sliver of new moon showing, and we had the surface of the old Windy all to ourselves.

"Do you want to try a trot?" I asked after we had walked a ways.

"*Yep!*"

I stepped old Hippo up to a trot and then to a canter. But I wouldn't let him gallop with Sil in the saddle behind me because—well, because I was afraid he might fall off. Now you might think it strange for me to worry about a a catfish falling into a river, which was his natural element, after all. Ah, but that was the bug in the begonias. It had been his natural element to begin with, but was it any longer?

So we took it easy that first night. We trotted up and down the river, kind of keeping an eye out for other catfish, but mainly just enjoying ourselves. I was so moved by the beauty of it all that I broke into song once more. If you ever want to try it, Johnny, the tune is the one for *The Streets of Laredo*.

> "*As I rode out on the old Windy River,*
> *As I trotted out on the river one night,*
> *Ridin' a hippo and totin' a catfish,*
> *It certainly was a remarkable sight!*"

And would you believe it? Sil began to join in. He went, "*Yip, yip, yip yiii!*" just like a coyote. Why, even old Hippo began to snort in time with the tune! We wound up riding and singing until the sun poked its way up over the Dismal Hills, and I began to grow worried that some nosy government investigator might drive by and see us. I don't know what kind of regulation we would be violating, but I'm sure they would find one somewhere.

Yes indeed, Johnny, those were wonderful nights, and the memory of them lingers to this day. But like all wonderful things, they had to come to an end—and a mighty sad and peculiar end it was, too.

XII.

It hurts to write this last sad passage, Johnny, but I have to tell you about the sad fate of old Sil. By then he was no longer little Sil. Nosir! He was putting on the pounds and growing longer and wider with every passing day. I figured that in another month or so he would be too big to fit in the saddle with me.

And you may not believe this, but he had reached the point where he spent almost the entire day out of the water. He would dive into his tub once or twice just to cool off, but when he came up he'd be sputtering and gasping. Talk about a metamorphosis!

It was right about then when Granny Grimoire sent me word that her time in exile was almost up and she would soon be heading back to her own dimension. She said it would be a good idea if she took old Hippo with her, and I had to agree. I'd grown really fond of that river horse and our gallops up and down the Windy, but I had to admit that at best Hippo would be stared at and exploited as a freak—while at worst some dang-fool hunter might bag him as a trophy.

Then there was the problem of no-longer-little Sil. A lung-breathing, fin-walking, mouth-yipping, stick-fetching catfish was likely to call attention to himself. I was already getting a notorious reputation throughout Snodgrass County. In fact, my continued association with Granny and her unearthly plants and critters could likely jeopardize the chances of my neighbors, the Finsters, being chosen as one of the Ten Most Ordinary Families in America.

But the moon was waxing toward full again, so I begged Granny to let me keep Hippo just a few more days so that I could be sure there were no more great galloping catfish along my stretch of the old Windy. She agreed, and on the night of the full moon Hippo, Sil and I set out on what would be our last ride together.

I had put all my problems aside because it was a perfect night for a ride on the river. Old Hippo's water shoes hardly caused a ripple as we moseyed along with just the hint of a breeze carrying the sounds of the shore to us. I could count individual crickets and track the flight of owls as they hooted. It was that calm and peaceful.

In fact, I should have realized it was just a little *too* calm and peaceful. Somebody somewhere was up to something. But what?

I got the answer in the very next instant when a big ripple roiled the surface of the old Windy and another catfish rose to the surface. This one was long and slim, and I could almost swear it had a curvaceous figure. It kind of lolled there on the surface and made some of those same little yipping sounds I'd heard Sil give out. I couldn't understand them, but Sil sure could!

"*Yip! Yip! Yipe! Yipe! Yiiiii!*" he answered. I felt him squirming in the saddle behind me. I knew he was fixing to bail out, and I tried to grab hold of him, because all of a sudden I realized what was calling to him.

"Hold on there, Sil!" I cried as I tried to keep hold of him. "That's a siren trying to lure you to your doom! That's a Lorelei calling to you if ever I saw one!" (Actually, Johnny, I've never seen one. But there are some situations where a guess is as good as a fact, and this surely was one of them.)

But this Lorelei's sudden appearance had startled old Hippo, and have you ever tried to hold on to a squirming catfish while keeping your seat on the back of a rearing and plunging hippopotamus? No, I didn't think so. Why, it was all I could do to stay in the saddle myself.

Poor Sil slithered right out of my grasp and plunged into the old Windy, trying his utmost to reach that tempting siren. But that poor catfish had changed so much during his time with me that he had completely forgotton how to swim.

Yep. I'm afraid poor Sil sank straight to the bottom and drowned!

The Skwookuss and the Humidaba

I.

Johnny, I called my place Ruination Farm because that's what all my friends said when I told them I was moving out to a little place six miles north of Nowhere.

"Grandpappy," they all said, "that place will be your ruination for sure!"

Well, so far it hasn't, but I have to admit there have been a few times when it came mighty close. Probably the closest was when I had to deal with that pesky skwookuss and that dreadful humidaba. You've never heard about those critters? Then I guess I'd better enlighten you on the subject.

It all began soon after the demise of Sil the cat-fish. I looked across the Windy River one morning and saw smoke coming from the Dismal Hills. At first I thought there might be a forest fire over there. Part of me hoped that wasn't so, but another part of me hoped it was.

Why was I halfway hoping it was a forest fire? Because that was the darkest, dankest, most dismal forest anyone ever had the misfortune to see. Half the trees wouldn't put out any leaves at all, and those that did produced leaves that were a sooty gray instead of green. So were the needles on the evergreens—which were evergrays instead. The undergrowth was nothing more than some scattered brush and weeds.

But what made things worse were the animals—or rather, the lack of animals. Nothing lived in the Dismal Hills except for those crows I told you about, and they stayed right on the edge within sight of the river and never ventured far into the forest itself.

Can you imagine walking through a forest without seeing or hearing any living critter? I tried it once, and it just was about the spookiest experience I ever had. I can see why the loggers called it quits and left almost a century ago. So when I saw that smoke, you can understand why a part of me hoped for a good catastrophic fire. It might actually improve the place.

However, soon after I saw the smoke, Granny Grimoire appeared and told me not to worry about it. She was finally getting ready to leave her place of exile, and part of her cleanup task was to burn all the unnatural plants she had brought with her.

"Granny, did you get a burning permit?" I asked her.

"Why do I need a permit to burn stuff that isn't supposed to exist in the first place?" she answered me. "If I'm burning nonexistent fuel, then wouldn't that make it a nonexistent fire?"

"Granny, you might think that way—and I might even be inclined to agree with you. But I'm afraid the government might have a different opinion."

"That's what the man who came out to see me said."

"Great galloping catfish, Granny! Did he give you a citation?"

"He didn't get the chance. I changed him into a bullfrog."

"Granny! You're not supposed to do things like that!"

"Why not?" she asked. "He was interfering with my work and being very obnoxious about it. Now he's a perfectly good bullfrog and probably performing a valuable service at this very minute—keeping the fly and larvae population in check."

"Look!" I said as severely as I dared, because you don't want to get too forceful with a witch, even a witch-in-exile. "Is that spell permanent or can it be undone?"

"Oh, it will wear off in a hundred of your years, give or take."

"Granny, that is cruel and unusual punishment! An adult human won't live another hundred years! Neither will an adult bullfrog!" I added as an afterthought.

"Well, I suppose I could change it to a hundred months. How would that be?"

"That's eight years, plus another four months. I'm pretty sure bullfrogs don't live that long either."

"How about a hundred weeks then?"

"That's almost two years." I considered for a bit and wondered just how I get myself into situations like this. Here I had started out to spend a perfectly normal morning, and all of a sudden I'm negotiating for some government agent's life. Could it be young Fiske, I thought. He was a little abrasive sometimes, and it's not a good idea to get abrasive with a witch.

"He might last a hundred weeks," I conceded, "but I wouldn't give him very good odds. "I doubt if he has the survival skills."

"A hundred days then. What do you say?"

"Hmm. Maybe fifty-fifty. You see, he probably doesn't know much about how to gather food or protect himself from predators."

"There aren't any around here except for the crows, and I'll have a word with them about leaving him alone." She drew herself up rather forcefully. "A hundred hours then, and that's my final offer!"

"That's just over four days. Can you get everything cleared away by then?"

"Piece of cake, as you humans say. You'll have to explain that saying to me sometime, Grandpappy."

"I will if you will keep your word," I said. "But right now you'd better get to work, and I expect to see that government agent in another four days!"

II.

By the following morning the Dismal Hills looked a lot less dismal. Why, I could swear I saw colors, actual colors, starting to appear here and there. That forest seemed to be slowly waking up, like someone coming out of a deep coma.

I wondered how that inspector-turned-bullfrog was making out, and I considered trying to catch him and put him in a pen to keep him safe. But I decided against it. He was an official government bullfrog, after all. So I would probably need an official government permit to catch him, and the Good Lord only knows where I could get one of those. Besides, it might distract and upset Granny in the middle of her work, and that was not a good idea. No, the government bullfrog would have to take his chances.

My own work kept me pretty busy all that day and most of the next. Chores have to be done, Johnny, no matter what else is going on in that big old world around you. So it was mid-afternoon on the following day when I looked up from my work to see Granny Grimoire standing beside me waiting to catch my attention. She had a worried look on her face that seemed to bode ill for the both of us.

"Grandpappy, I have a small confession to make," she said in a tone that suggested it was somewhat larger than small.

"Do tell!" I replied. "I never knew witches confessed to anything." I must admit I was a little sarcastic. I get that way when I become nervous, and her manner and tone right then were enough to scare the blue jimhickies out of me.

"You see," she continued, "I was digging up and burning all the unnatural plants in my unnatural garden, and I've got just about all of them disposed of."

"Well, Granny, that sounds like good news to me. So why are you upset?"

"Well, my devilberries had just ripened, and they were the best—I suppose you would say the worst—crop I'd ever raised here in this dimension. So..."

She shook her head and her voice trailed off, and doggone if she didn't look just like a child who'd been caught doing something naughty.

"So?" I prompted her.

"So I picked a bunch and made myself a nice big devilberry pie."

"Granny, I hope you don't intend to offer me a slice. It doesn't sound like something that would agree with me."

"Oh, it would kill you," she assured me. "Anyway, I couldn't do that even if I wanted to. You see, it tasted so good that I ate the whole thing all at one sitting."

"Is that bad?" I prompted again. She was taking her time getting to the point.

"I'm afraid it is. You see, too much devilberry pie before bedtime always gives me indigestion and terrible nightmares."

"I guess I'm sorry to hear it, but what does this have to do with me?"

"In my dimension nightmares can become real. They take physical shape, and if you don't corral them as soon as you wake up—well, I'm afraid they get loose. Four of mine did this morning."

"Dare I ask what kind of critters they were?"

"A skwookuss, a humidaba, a hoodukai and a rovelgoven. I think I have the last two pretty well rounded up, but I wanted to warn you that the skwookuss and the humidaba might be headed your way."

"Great galloping catfish, Granny! What do you expect *me* to do?"

"Just keep them contained while I deal with the others. And don't worry! They're not nearly as bad as the hoodukai or the rovelgoven."

That last bit of information was not all that comforting. How was I supposed to deal with two monsters I knew absolutely nothing about? What were they like? Where were their weaknesses? How should I arm myself against them? Was there anything in my attic that would help? (*Dang!* I'm going to have to clean that place out sometime!)

Well, I didn't have much time to ponder these questions. Granny hadn't been gone more than a minute when I saw one of them coming up from the riverbank.

III.

At first I wasn't sure if it was one critter or two, because I saw two heads. One was looking right at me, while the other faced the opposite direction. But it only had two arms and two legs. When it got a bit closer, I saw that they were both right arms, and both its lower appendages were right legs as well.

Because of this, it moved with a curious lurching motion, since one leg had to walk backward while the other moved forward. For a moment I nearly laughed at the sight it presented—but that was only for a moment.

You see, Johnny, as that critter got closer, I realized it stood upwards of nine feet tall, and it carried a big old club in each of its big old hands. Furthermore, it looked like it knew how to use them. It must have been six feet from shoulder to shoulder,

and those two heads were mounted on a pair of necks as big around as telephone poles.

And talk about ugly! I believe I once said that Granny Grimoire could win the annual Snodgrass County Ugly Person Contest hands down, didn't I? Well, not if this critter was entered! *Maybe* it might have finished second behind the Medusa—she's the monster in Greek mythology that would turn you to stone if you looked square at her—on the all-time ugly list, but it would be a mighty close second. And I hadn't seen the second face yet—it might be even worse!

The critter looked to be covered all over with coarse dark hair. But it did wear a rough garment, made from some kind of skin, that covered it from chest to knee and was held up by a strap that passed between its heads and over where its left shoulders would have been if it had any.

"Well now," I said to myself. "This looks to be one of Granny's missing nightmares. I wonder now, which one is it?"

As if to answer me, the mouth in its ugly old head opened wide , and I heard it rumble, "Skwoo!" Then it did a very curious thing. The arm beside the head facing me reached around and bopped the back of the opposite head with its club. That must have been some kind of signal, because both legs took a step forward. This, of course, brought the critter around in a half-circle, so that the second head now faced me. It was every bit as ugly as the first one.

"Kusss!" it rumbled.

"All right," I said to myself. "I guess that answers that question. This must be the skwookuss. Now, how do I deal with it?" Granny had been in too much of a hurry to leave any instructions.

While I was pondering this particular problem, the skwookuss must have been thinking the same thing about me, and it reached a decision before I did. Its second arm reached around and bopped its first head, and it performed another half-circle two-step.

"Skwoo!" the first head rumbled in a downright unfriendly manner. Then it started lurching toward me, one leg moving forward while the other was striding backward. It may not be the most efficient way to move, but it does cover the ground.

I decided right then and there that this was no time to begin a friendly discussion, so I set out to put a little distance between us. But I'm afraid it's been many a year since I ran the anchor leg on Snodgrass County High School's record-setting mile relay team—a record that still stands, by the way. True, I did hold the advantage of having both legs pointed in the same direction, but they were considerably shorter than those on the skwookuss.

It soon became obvious that I was maybe a shade faster, but the skwookuss held the advantage when it came to endurance. It looked mighty determined too. In the long run, if it came to that, I couldn't outlast it, and I was pretty dang certain I couldn't outfight it. So how was I going to escape?

"Grandpappy," I told myself, "you're going to have to *outthink* it. Use the old noodle! That's your only way to survive!"

So, as I hoofed it up the pasture and across the road, I stole a couple of quick glances back over my shoulder at that critter and tried to calculate just what and where its weak points might be. I noticed it paused every hundred yards or so to switch around. The signal seemed to be a bop on one head with the opposite club and a "Skwoo!" or a "Kuss!"—depending on which head was facing backward at the time.

Johnny, it was those clubs that gave me the idea.

IV.

You see, back in the days when I was the all-star second baseman for our local semi-pro team, the Snodgrass County Sidewinders, I had an old iron-wood fungo bat that I always swung in the on-deck circle. Of course, it was way too heavy to take up to the plate. But after half a minute of swinging it in that circle, my regular bat felt like it had been corked. I'd go up to the plate knowing I could get around on anything and feeling like I could smack any pitch within reach clear out of the park. And I did just that on several occasions too.

I still had that old bat out in my barn. I figured if I could get to it, then I stood a fighting chance. And a fighting chance was all I was asking for right then.

I put on a burst of speed to gain a little ground, then ducked into the barn, grabbed up the old fungo bat, zipped out the back way and hollered to attract the skwookuss' attention. I didn't want it running in there after me, of course. Several of my own critters were penned up in their stalls and helpless, and that skwookuss' socialization skills seemed to be somewhat underdeveloped.

So I ran for a bend in the old Windy River instead. You might think that was foolish, since I would be cornering myself and doing that critter's work for it. In fact, you might be wondering why I didn't just jump in my truck, drive to town and fetch the sheriff and a few deputies to deal with it.

Well, consider what I would have to say to them. *There's this nine-foot critter with two heads, two right legs and arms and an awful mean disposition. It's chasing me all around my farm, and I fear it means to do me great bodily harm, if not worse. Could you please come out and help me deal with it?*

No, I was going to have to deal with this critter myself.

But I'd come up with the germ of an idea by then, and all the while I was running for the riverbank, it was developing and growing in my head.

Now what do you suppose there was down on the banks of the old Windy that might help me out of my predicament? Rocks, Johnny! That's what! The bank was covered with them, all worn smooth by the river, and a good many about the size and almost as round as a baseball. I gathered a dozen or two as quickly as I could while I waited for the skwookuss to catch up with me. It had slowed down and was taking its time, now that it seemed to have me penned in by the river.

As that ugly old critter drew close, I picked up a rock, lobbed it into the air and took a swing as it came down.

Whock! The rock arced out over the river and hit with a splash about halfway across.

"Think you can beat that?" I called out. I don't think that skwookuss understood my words, but the challenge in my voice was obvious.

"Skwooo!" it answered as it bopped itself on the head once more and did another two-step turn-around. I figured the second head wanted to see what it had missed, so I tossed up another rock and took another swing.

Whock! The second rock went about as far as the first and hit the old Windy with a nice little splash.

"Kusss!" cried that ugly head. It bopped itself again and turned another half-circle so that the skwoo side faced me again.

I picked up another rock and the skwoo waggled its club and shifted its foot just like a batter digging in at the plate. "Okay, here it comes, you despicable nose-picker!" I said, and I lobbed a nice easy batting-practice slow ball to it.

"Skwooo!" it cried and swung.

Whock! Even with just one arm, it drove that rock a good thirty feet beyond where I had batted mine, and that ugly nightmare's momentum carried it around in a full circle, kicking up dirt behind it. Johnny, that's what I was hoping for!

"Skwoooo!" it cried. I could swear it grinned at me, as if it were saying, "Pitcher, is that all the better you can do?"

"Kussss!" cried the second head, and I'll bet that meant, "Hey! It's my turn now!" Then it rapped the skwoo rather smartly with its club, and the critter took another half-turn. But the skwoo half seemed to do so reluctantly.

"All right then, let's see if you can top your partner," I said as I fed the kuss another slow and easy one.

Whock! I'm not sure if the kuss topped the skwoo, but I'd say it equaled it. The rock soared out over the river and splashed down well beyond anything I could hit. Again the critter's momentum carried it around in a full circle and kicked up a lot more dirt.

"Kussss!" it cried, and I'll be that meant, "Pitcher, you've got nothing!"

"Skwooo!" cried the other head as its arm rapped the kuss even more smartly on its ugly old noggin. I could see where a good argument might lead to a pair of goshawful headaches, and that was just what I was trying to start.

This time I put a little more zip on the old rock, and that critter swung even harder. That rock hit better than three-quarters of the way across the river.

"Skwoooo!" cried the head, and I took that to mean, "Pitcher, you'd better head for the showers if that's all the better you can do!"

A whack from the second club cut short the skwoo's triumph and sent the critter around in another half circle. The skwoo wasn't happy about it, but the kuss dug in and waved its club like it was going to show me some *real* hitting.

"All right, you ugly old cuss of a kuss!" I challenged it. "Let's see you hit one of my fast ones!" You see, Johnny, while my usual position was second base, I did pitch a little short relief once in a while. So I could put a little heat on the old rock if I wanted to—although I had never tried it with an actual rock before.

I wanted to see if it could handle the high heat, so I fed it a letter-high fastball. (Well, it would have been letter-high if that ugly critter had any letters on that piece of drapery it wore.) I then got an instant answer to my question.

Whock! That rock soared away like an artillery shell and landed in what would have been the centerfield bleachers if we had been in a ballpark instead of on a riverbank. As it was, it came within twenty feet of making the far bank. That ugly monster again spun in a full circle and kicked up more dirt.

"Kussss!" it cried, and I took that to mean, "Thought you could get the old fastball by me, huh? Let's see you try it again!"

"Skwoooo!" the other head objected and rapped the kuss rather sharply on the back of its noggin. Apparently, it was not about to be cheated out of a turn at bat. Still, it took two more bops and three angry *skwooo*s before it got its chance.

Meanwhile, I was searching for just the right rock. That critter could get around on my high hard one easily enough, but could it handle a slider low and away? I went into a full windup and let one fly.

Whifff! Just as I'd hoped, the skwoo was way out in front and six inches over that slider as it broke down and away. It spun two full circles and kicked up a lot more dirt before it got itself back under control.

"Kuss! Kuss! Kuss! Kuss!" cried the other head. I do believe it was laughing at the skwoo, and the skwoo didn't like that one bit.

V.

See, Johnny, the conclusion I had reached was this. As long as those two heads cooperated with each other, I didn't stand a chance. But if I could get them to quarreling with themselves, then each might cancel the other out. So I selected another rock and set out to slip a slider by the kuss as well.

Whifff! This time the slider broke down and in, and the kuss was a foot out in front and half a foot over as it spun another two circles and kicked up more dirt. Why was I so interested in that dirt it kicked up? Let me tell you, Johnny.

That critter had one mean set of claws on it, that's for sure! Foot-wise, it reminded me a bit of the world's biggest badger—and you know how those critters can dig! That skwookuss was boring a hole in the ground with its claws, and it was just like two big drill bits ripping through soft wood! That hole was already more than a foot deep. Now if I could keep it spinning and fighting with itself—why, it might dig itself right down out of sight. Or at least deep enough that I could trap it.

Meanwhile, it was the skwoo's turn to laugh, which it promptly did, and threw in a bop on the kuss' head for good measure. The kuss bopped it right back, and for a moment it looked like I might have that fight I was hoping for. But it managed to get its tempers back under control, though just barely. All the while I was hunting for two more perfect rocks.

It was the skwoo that now faced me, but I had calculated that the kuss was the one with the shorter temper—though probably not by much. So I fed the skwoo a straight fast one right down the middle with no movement on it. The critter's eyes lit up with anticipation, and it took a mighty rip at that old rock.

Whock! That rock was no more than five feet from the far bank when it splashed down. The force of that des-nose-picable critter's swing spun it three times around the way its claws worked reminded me of a corkscrew digging its way down into a cork. Of course, a corkscrew doesn't kick up quite as much dirt.

"Kusss!" cried the other half as it rapped the skwoo in a downright unfriendly way. I could guess what it was saying. "Give me my turn and I'll *really* show you how to belt one!"

It dug in with its claws and pounded the ground with its club just like the old poem about Casey at the Bat. Do you know what I've never liked about that poem, Johnny? They never gave any credit to the pitcher who got him out on three straight strikes. Okay, maybe I'm getting off the subject just a bit, but stay with me—because this explains just how I bamboozled that old skwookuss.

You see, that pitcher had brains, and that's what he used to get old Casey to whiff. He knew all about Casey's pride, see, and he was sure Casey would take two strikes just to build up the anticipation and suspense. So he fed him two straight fast ones right down the pipe and, sure enough, Casey let them go by."

(No, Johnny, I wasn't the pitcher that day. I'm old, but not that old. But I've been in situations like that and pitched may way out of them, so I can just about read that pitcher's thoughts. He must have been a genius.)

Let me climb into that pitcher's head for a second, because that's just what I did down on the banks of the old Windy. That first pitch was likely a straight fastball, and the second even faster. So I'll bet Casey figured the pitcher would put everything he had on the third and try to hum it by him—and that's how the pitcher got him.

Johnny, I'll bet he threw him a slowdown. You don't see that pitch anymore because it's…well…sort of against the rules. You have to scuff the ball and doctor it up a mite to make it work, and they won't let you do that nowadays. But long ago you could get away with throwing one occasionally—and it sure was a nasty pitch!

The slowdown starts out like a fastball, and for the first 40-45 feet it really hums along. But 15-20 feet out from the plate it sort of hits the brakes, and when it plops into the catcher's mitt, it's got no more velocity than the ceremonial first pitch some dignitary tosses out to start the game.

But by the time the batter realizes this, it's too late. He's already swung. That's what got Casey out, and that's just how I planned to get that skwookuss.

Granted, the circumstances were a little different. I didn't have a baseball to doctor up, and this sure wasn't a friendly game. But I had an old river rock just about the size of a baseball, plus a jar of horse liniment in the pocket of my overalls. You see, I was fixing to do a little doctoring before Granny came to call, and that particular concoction was my own special private recipe. It could do wonders for an ailing horse, so I figured it might have some effect on a river rock as well.

So as the skwookuss waved its club and snarled, I smeared that rock with liniment and snarled right back. Then I took a full windup and let fly.

Whifff! The kuss swung so hard that critter spun around a full three times. Matter of fact, it nearly connected the third time around. But that sloweddown rock plopped harmlessly to the ground just a few feet behind the kuss and right in front of the skwoo, who seemed delighted by the miss.

"Skwoo-hoo-hoo-hoo!" it cried as it whacked the rock with its own club and sent what would have been a wicked liner right over second base and clipped the kuss right behind the ear as it finished the swing. I translated those remarks to be, "Kuss, you are strictly a bush-league, banjo hitter!"

"Kuss-kuss-kuss-*kuss!*" the other half replied, and whacked the skwoo right back. I'm not sure how those remarks translated, but somehow I don't think they were meant for polite society.

"Skwoo-hoo-*ooo!*" the first head countered—and then the fight was on!

That ugly old critter began to spin in a circle as each half tried to chase the other! It whacked itself on the head and bellowed "Skwoo!" or "Kuss" each time it landed a blow. And all the while its claws were throwing up the dirt and digging it in deeper and deeper.

I watched the combat for a few minutes and then headed back to the barn, where I picked up a bag of

Hercules Brand Extra Quick-Drying Cement, a shovel and a couple of buckets. These I piled into a wheelbarrow and made my way back to the scene of battle. By this time that skwookuss was in up past its waist and spinning around and throwing up dirt like it meant to burrow its way clear through to China.

Johnny, it almost made me dizzy just watching it. But its actions didn't surprise me—not in the least. Do you know why?

Well, I'd read of a similar occurrence in the story of Jason and the Argonauts. If you remember (and you *have* read that, haven't you?), Jason planted the teeth of a dragon he had just killed, and each tooth instantly grew into an armed warrior—and they were all of a mind to kill him and his men. But Jason tossed a stone into the middle of that group, and the one it hit thought the man next to him had done it. So he drew his sword and went at him. But they wounded a third, who attacked a fourth. And before you knew it, that whole bunch had wiped each other out. And that's just what the skwookuss was doing too!

By the time I had the cement ready it had slowed down quite a bit, and the whacks it was giving itself had become little more than love-taps (to it, that is— just one would have knocked me into the middle of next week). It wasn't going to make it clear to China, but it had dug itself in clear up to its necks by the time both heads gave a sigh and apparently passed out.

I shoveled some of the dirt back in, packed it good and tight, then added the cement until I had that critter encased right up to its pair of ugly chinny-chin-chins. I hoped it would dry as quickly as the directions on the bag promised—and it did!

"Granny!" I shouted across the river. "I've got the skwookuss for you! It'a all wrapped up and ready for delivery!"

Now, Johnny, there is a moral to the first part of this story, and here it is. When dealing with certain kinds of monsters, a good working knowledge of baseball psychology and Greek mythology comes in mighty handy.

VI.

Granny arrived just a few minutes later. I was never sure just how she crossed the Windy River, but there she was. When she saw how I had that skwookuss packaged up and ready for delivery, she jumped higher than anyone her age has a right to jump and clapped her hands for joy.

"Amazing!" she cried. "Why, all I dared hope for was that you could keep it occupied until I could get back over."

"All in a morning's work," I said as modestly as I could.

"I haven't been idle either," she assured me. "Matter of fact, I've disposed of the rovelgoven and the hoodukai."

"Well, that's wonderful, Granny!"

"Almost wonderful, but not quite," she corrected me. "You see, the humidaba is still on the loose somewhere."

"*Somewhere* is kind of vague, Granny," I remarked. "How big an area are we talking about here? Far as that goes, how much of a humidaba are we talking about? What does it look like? How dangerous is it, and how do you deal with it?"

"You ask an awful lot of questions," she observed.

"Then provide me with some answers," I replied.

"I'd best not. You see, I'm trying not to think about it. If I describe it to you, then I have to picture it in my mind. And if I do that—well, it's like feeding it. Picturing it makes it grow bigger and stronger—and nastier."

"Then what do we do?"

"It's probably still over on my side of the river. I'll go back and hunt for it as soon as I've disposed of this skwookuss. You'd best stay close around your house until I give you the all clear. You might even consider clearing out for a while."

"Granny!" I said with as much dignity as I could muster. "There's nobody, no monster, no critter of any kind, that's ever going to run me off my own land! Besides, I have critters of my own here that depend on me. Should I run off and leave them here at the mercy of something out of your nightmares? How could I live with myself if I did such a cowardly act?"

"That's very noble of you, Grandpappy. Very foolish, but very noble. Stay here then, if you must. Just hope I find it before it finds you!"

And with that, she turned back to deal with the skwookuss, while I hurried on up to the house to prepare myself for another battle.

But just how do you prepare yourself to fight something when you have absolutely no idea of what that something is? A humidaba might be anything from a bug to a dragon. Would you swat it? Stomp it? Stab it? Shoot it?

As far as that goes, what would the humidaba's intentions be? Would it seek to devour me? Squish me? Or maybe play ring around the rosey? I dismissed that last guess as highly unlikely and concluded that there wasn't much to do but wait and hope and pray that Granny would take the job of dealing with it off my hands. But I had my doubts about that. Some awful strange things occur out at Ruination Farm, and I had a feeling this humidaba critter was going to be one of them.

VII.

Now pause a moment to ponder this point, Johnny. Why me? Why Ruination Farm? Couldn't that critter just as easily head for my neighbors after it crossed the river—*if* it had crossed the river to begin with?

Consider my neighbors to the north, the Finsters. Might not that humidaba choose to head for their place instead? Or what about the Jenkins boys across the road and down a ways to the south? Wouldn't it be just as easy for that critter to pay a social call on them? But no, Johnny. Even as I tried to come up with positive thoughts, I knew it wasn't going to be the case.

The Finsters were so ordinary that they were odds-on favorites to be picked as one of the Ten Most

Ordinary Families in America! In fact, an aura of ordinary radiated from their ordinary house and spread across their ordinary land like an invisible screen, and I doubted if anything out of the ordinary could ever penetrate it. Why, even I had a tough time making it up their ordinary driveway to their ordinary front door when I went to call on them, and I'm hardly more than a little bit out of the ordinary.

No, it definitely wouldn't be the Finsters.

The Jenkins boys, on the other hand, didn't radiate anything. (I think I told you about them in connection with the episode of the popapples at the Greater Snodgrass County Fair, didn't I?) They weren't really bad folks at all. It's just that Mother Nature tended to neglect replacing their bulbs when they burned out. You can't really be terrified of something if you are unable to comprehend what terror is. Abner didn't understand anything more complex than hot dogs, and Homer wasn't interested in anything he couldn't take apart and then fail to put back together.

Nope. Unless that humidaba was a hot-dog production kit that could be disassembled, the Jenkins boys wouldn't even notice it. Thus, if it crossed the river, that humidaba, whatever it was, had just one possible destination—and that was Ruination Farm.

And I was right. I had just moseyed out behind the barn to see if I could spot anything suspicious when I heard a rustling in the bushes over to my left. Then a head popped up and looked square at me. I guess it wanted a really good look because it rose higher and higher and higher—until I was looking at the biggest gosh-darn snake I had ever seen in all my days on this earth!

"Granny!" I cried as soon as I could collect my senses. "I'd sure appreciate it if you got over here pretty darn quick, because I think I've found what you're seeking!"

But Granny never answered me a word. Either she was still occupied with the skwookuss or she was searching way off in the wrong direction.

Now all the time I'd been trying to get Granny's attention, the head on that old serpent had been rising higher and higher into the air. *Good Lord!* I thought. *Is that critter ever going to stop elevating itself?*

Well, it finally stopped with its ugly old head was sixteen or eighteen feet clear of the ground. I guess it wanted to spy out the land and see what was available for the taking. And wouldn't you know it? I was the nearest moving object. Its ugly old head—Johnny, it was the size of a beach ball—fixed itself on me, and its horrible mouth split open in a big, broad grin.

Thank goodness for one small thing! I thought as I examined its dental work. *No fangs, so at least it's probably not poisonous.*

But, Johnny, I'm afraid my mind had spoken its piece too soon.

Click! The sound was just like a switchblade knife snapping open. All of a sudden a fang that must have been close to a foot long appeared in that ugly critter's open jaw!

Click! Here came the second fang! A saber-toothed tiger, had one been present, would have died from envy right on the spot.

Click! A third fang appeared right between the first two! It was right about this time that I concluded that the more distance I could put between myself and that serpent, the better it would be for me. So I started backing away at a pretty smart clip.

But the serpent must have decided to become more personally acquainted, as it slithered out from behind the bushes and began to head my way. It must have been a few feet longer than a telephone pole from the tip of its nose to the tip of its tail, but, mind you, that was just an estimate. I was in no mood to try for an accurate measurement.

"Mr. Humidaba, for that is who I believe you are," I said as politely as I could under the circumstances. "I am sorry to take leave of you, but I've just remembered a previous engagement that I am going to make as quickly as I can!"

And with that, Johnny, I took off as fast as I could run!

VIII.

After two or three hundred yards I glanced back over my shoulder to see how we were doing. It looked like I might have a slight advantage in the speed department, but the humidaba probably held the edge when it came to endurance. I considered an all-out sprint for the truck in the hope I could get it started and be on my way before that super-sized serpent could catch up to me.

Then something happened that changed my mind.

You see, I had just sprinted past the chicken coop when one of my old roosters wandered out to see what all the fuss and commotion was about. The humidaba fixed its cold reptilian eye on it, and its gaze just froze that old rooster right on the spot. I mean, it was transfixed as surely as if it had been nailed to the ground! For a moment I actually felt relieved. I hoped that serpent might take a notion to swallow that rooster whole and then go nice and torpid for a while, like a normal snake would. But the humidaba apparently had other ideas.

Without hardly breaking a slither, that humidaba flicked its head to one side and gave that petrified rooster one teeny little nip as it slid on past. I guess it intended to give me a demonstration of just how potent its venom was. If so, it was a mighty convincing demonstration. That poor old rooster didn't even kick! It just toppled over, turned black and swelled up like a balloon. And when it couldn't swell any more, it popped!

It was then I realized that if I drove off, I would be abandoning all my animals and leaving them at the mercy of that ugly old serpent, and for some reason I didn't think that mercy ranked very high on a humidaba's list of virtues. So I abandoned the notion of fleeing the battlefield and headed for the house instead.

That horrible humidaba paused at my truck just long enough to jab my two front tires and put them out of commission. Not only did they go flat—why, I could smell the scorched rubber from a hundred yards away! In fact, as I took a quick glance back along that serpent's trail, I could see the scorch marks in the ground showing where it had passed.

This critter was even more formidable than the skwookuss!

I was trying my doggondest to come up with a plan for dealing with it as I nipped inside the house and bolted the door behind me. Now you might wonder why, in a desperate situation like that, would I choose to enclose myself? Well, the house was familiar ground, and it contained weapons I could use to fight back with.

No, Johnny, I didn't have a gun. But I did have my brains, and I was working them as hard as I could to come up with a plan as I watched that ugly old serpent come slithering across the yard. It is indeed amazing how fast the mind can work when it absolutely has to. Before that humidaba could reach my door, I had a plan in mind, a weapon in hand—and I was ready to fight back!

You see, it might have been easier for that serpent to come in through a window, but I had a feeling it would try for the door. I had just slammed it in its ugly old face, after all, so I calculated it would want to show me that something as puny as a door was no match for its evil intentions. That's what the old-time Greeks called *hubris*, or the sin of pride. I wasn't sure if this was an old-time Greek serpent or not. But I had the feeling it was a prideful varmint, and I aimed to use that pride against it.

Sure enough, it did just that. *Wham!* That humidaba struck my door a blow that shook the whole house and broke three more teacups! But more important was the fact that its fangs penetrated all the way through—and that was a solid oak door, Johnny! But that is what I hoped would happen. Those fangs stuck out a good six inches on my side of the door, and before that humidaba could pull them back out, it was my turn to strike!

My weapon was my old ballpeen hammer. Before that serpent could pull itself free—*Whop! Whop! Whop! Whop! Whop! Whop!* I had clinched those fangs down so tightly that there was no way under heaven that critter was going to pull 'em out again!

"Hah! You obsnifferous old scaleywag!" I called out to it. "How do you like dealing with somebody who knows how to fight back?"

Apparently that humidaba didn't like it one bit. It gave a goshalmighty yank, and would you believe it? That critter pulled my front door right off its hinges! I watched that door bounce and crash around the yard as that serpent tried to work its clinched-over fangs free. But I had hammered them down good and tight, so there was no way that was going to happen——or so I thought.

IX.

Remember what I said happened to that rooster, Johnny? How it swelled up until it popped like a balloon? Well, the same thing happened with my door. It must have been the venom that humidaba deposited in the wood when it struck. Whatever the case, that door began to swell like an infected blister—which is sort of what it was, I guess. Within seconds it had doubled in width and breadth, and dang-near tripled in thickness.

Something was going to have to give, and that something was the humidaba's fangs!

That swollen door pulled the fangs right out of that ugly serpent's mouth slicker than any dentist could have done with a pair of forceps—had there been a dentist around foolish enough to make the attempt. That obsnifferous old scaleywag looked hurt, amazed and vexed all at the same time. Then it gave me a glare of pure malice and began slithering my way once again. That old serpent had had grit and determination, Johnny! I'll have to give it credit for that!

But I was waiting for it with my next weapon in hand, and when it drew to within a few feet of me, I put that weapon to good use. Care to guess what that weapon was? All my remaining popapple pips—that's what!

When that serpent opened its ugly mouth in an attempt to spray some venom my way, I flung those pips right down its gullet! I know reptiles are cold-blooded, but I was hoping that humidaba's innards were warm enough for those pips to do their thing—and I was right once more!

Whump! Bump! Thump! Crump! I could see that serpent's innards bulge and swell as more than a hundred pips went off! But that obsnifferous old scaleywag must have possessed a stainless steel gastro-intestinal track and a set of reinforced, double-boiler-plated bowels! It did look mighty discomforted for a few moments, like someone with a sudden attack of the galloping colleywobbles. But then it gave out with a tremendous snort and started after me again!

I knew this couldn't go on much longer. I was running out of weapons and running out of options too. My truck was out of commission and my house had no front door. Granted, the humidaba had lost its fangs, but it still had its venom. Furthermore, it seemed to have a desire to wrap me in its embrace and give me a hug to end all hugs! And Johnny, I didn't feel the least bit affectionate that day!

My one hope seemed to be Granny Grimoire riding to the rescue like the cavalry in those westerns I used to take you to see. But that only happens in the movies, and here I was with a real-life crisis on my hands and not a trooper or a witch-in-exile to be seen. If I was going to be saved, it looked like I would have to do the job myself.

Think, Grandpappy! I said to myself. *Use that old noodle! You've overcome one incredible monster already today. Surely you can manage one more!*

Well, I could think of only one thing, and that seemed like a long shot. But I had to do something and do it mighty fast! So I sprinted back through the house and out the back door, pausing only long enough to grab a box off the shelf right over my stove. That determined old serpent was right on my tail, and I hoped old Hairball had sense enough to stay hidden and well out of the way—which he did. He may be a worthless, paranoid cat, but he's sure not stupid.

As soon as I was well clear of the house and close by the barn, I turned at bay. The humidaba opened its mouth and came for me again. When it was close enough that I couldn't miss, I chucked that box right into its ugly old mouth, and it swallowed it down before it realized what it was doing. Johnny, that's what I had hoped for!

You see, that was a full box of baking soda that I kept right over the stove to use in case of a grease fire. I was calculating that old serpent's innards had already turned those popapples into the most potent cider vinegar known or unknown to man—and you know what happens when you mix vinegar and baking soda! I said some mighty quick prayers that my calculations were correct, and sure enough. They were.

That humidaba stopped dead in its tracks and began to swell up just like that poor old rooster it had slain. But I didn't think it would pop—not without a little help, that is. So I ran into the barn and came out with my final weapon—my trusty pitchfork!

I believe I told you once that I ran on the Snodgrass County High track team back in my early days. Well, I was also pretty good with the javelin—though modesty compels me to add that I was only the second-best thrower on the team.

Nonetheless, I grabbed that pitchfork and started my approach. Of course, a pitchfork is a far cry from a javelin, and I doubted if I could fling it more than thirty or forty feet. But I wasn't concerned with distance just then. All I wanted to do was hit the target.

By this time the humidaba was so swollen from end to end that I do believe its circumference would have equaled that of an old-growth redwood log. Its ugly face had the look of someone suffering an attack of the bilious constipation, and its hide was stretched as taut as a drumhead. I could actually see the skin between its scales.

Yes sir, that obsnifferous old scaleywag was finally vulnerable, but I knew I had to strike quickly before it could find relief at one end or the other. So

I went into my three crossover steps and then flung that pitchfork as hard as I could! The results were sure spectacular!

When those four tines pierced its hide, I heard a *Ffffssshhh!* Then that humidaba took off backwards around the barnyard, just like a balloon when you release the nozzle all of a sudden. I had to duck several times as it passed overhead. When it finally flopped back to earth, it did look a bit like a big empty balloon, although frankly it reminded me more of a gigantic toothpaste tube that had been squeezed and pressed and squeezed some more, until all the paste had been squeezed out.

Now I wasn't sure just how long this condition would last—my experience with humidabas being rather limited, after all. So, as quickly as I could, I slipped on a pair of latex gloves, ran to the tail and began to roll that old serpent up as tightly as I could. Then I took a few strands of bailing wire and secured it.

When it was all neatly trussed and tied, I called out, "Granny! Come and collect your critter!" And of course it was right then, after all the hard work had been done, that she showed up.

X.

"Grandpappy! This is amazing!" Granny cried when she saw the baled humidaba I had prepared for her. "Two monsters secured in one afternoon! I didn't think a single human could ever do that!"

"Shucks!" I replied as modestly as I could (because I do have to admit I was feeling just a bit proud of myself). "All it took was a little knowledge of basic chemistry and physics, plus a nodding acquaintance with the classics, a bit of sports psychology and some understanding of the workings of good and evil."

"Could you explain that last part for me?" she said.

"Easily," I replied. "Anyone so all-fired puffed up with himself is likely to be all hollow inside, since pride, greed and evil will all feed on one another. All I really did was give those critters a chance to self-destruct, and they did just that."

"Did they cause you much damage, Grandpappy? I do feel kind of responsible."

The total casualties on my side come to one rooster, two tires on my truck and a front door," I informed her.

"Let me replace them for you then," she offered.

"Uh...Granny, I don't think that would be a very good idea."

"Just listen a minute! I can get you a perpetual rooster. You can have him for dinner whenever you want. Just save the bones and feathers, store them overnight in the special coop I'll provide you, and by the next morning he'll be good as new again. Just think what that will do for your food budget!"

"Granny, I just don't think...."

"Now as for your door, I can whip up one of my specials for you. It will lock or unlock only on your command, and it can be just like one of your two-way mirrors. You will be able to see right through it to whoever is outside, but no one will be able to see in. How would you like that?"

"It's very nice, but..."

"And as for those tires—well, why don't I just replace your whole truck? I'll give you one that runs on air. Or if you'd like to drive it on the river bottom or under the sea, just flip a switch and the engine will run on water—either fresh or salt! And not only is it watertight and pressurized, you'll be able to fly it too! I can give it a ceiling of 40,000 feet and a speed close to mach-2! That's in the air, of course. Don't try it that fast on the ground. What do you say to that?"

"Granny, I know you're being kind and generous, and I really do appreciate your offer. If I were still young and full of beans and vinegar—well, I just might take you up on one or two of those offers. But your gifts seem to have a way of getting me into trouble, and your attempts at playing with nature have produced some rather unfortunate consequences. You've certainly made my life, well, *memorable*. I will say that. But I think I'll settle for a normal door, regular tires and an ordinary rooster. And if you don't mind, I will get them for myself.'

"Are you sure there's nothing I can do for you?" she asked.

"Just clean up after yourself and depart as soon as possible," I replied. "Dispose of that skwookuss and humidaba and whatever stray unnatural critters you may have up in the Dismal Hills, and I will be well satisfied."

"I will do that," she promised, and I turned and walked back to the house to call Myer O'Dwyer down at the Greater Snodgrass County Chamber of Commerce. He owed me a favor after all the catfish

I provided, and he was a man who didn't ask questions or spread reports. I knew I could have a new door, new tires and a new rooster before day's end, and no one need know the story behind them.

When I looked back over my shoulder, both Granny and the baled-up humidaba were gone, and I must admit I breathed a king-size sigh of relief.

XI.

By morning I could tell that Granny had left the Dismal Hills for good. At least I *hoped* it was for good. How could I tell? Well, those hills were blossoming out in all their glory. We were having springtime in October over there. I guess those hills had a century of the dismals to make up for, and they weren't about to let a little something like a calendar get in their way.

When the clouds rolled in from the west, as they always do in October, they would split apart as they passed over those hills, and the sunlight just beamed down on all the vegetation that had been so neglected during Granny's residency. At night it would cloud up, and a gentle rain would fall for four or five hours. I'm not sure if this was Granny's work or Mother Nature's or the Good Lord's—or maybe all three in collaboration. But whoever it was, those hills were mighty thankful—and they showed it.

But I still had one more item of business to take care of…

What had happened to that official government inspector who had been foolish enough to confront Granny and had wound up being transformed into a bullfrog? Could he survive that hundred-hour spell? If he did survive, how was I going to explain things to him? If he didn't, how could I explain it to those who came looking for him? The rest of his agency must have missed him by now.

But then again, knowing the government, maybe they hadn't.

My first thought was to row across the old Windy, prowl the banks and catch every likely-looking bullfrog I came across. I'd keep them all safely penned up until the balance of the hundred-hour spell had passed. Then I would know if any happened to be a government agent.

But, on the other hand, if one of them was young Fiske or one of his associates, he might hurt himself considerably changing back to human form in something as small as a frog pen. Now if I built it large enough to hold a human, would I then be guilty of false imprisonment after the frog turned human? It as enough to give a man a case of the blue jimhickies. Princesses had it lots easier. All they had to do was kiss the dang critters.

So I decided the best thing to do was wait until the hundred hours were just about up, then cross the river and try to latch on to that agent right after he became officially human again. Granny had been a bit vague about just when she had put the spell on him, but I calculated the time as best I could. Then I added four days plus four hours and rowed myself across the old Windy when I figured the spell was about to end.

Oh my, Johnny! Had those woods ever transformed themselves in just a few days! The sunlight filtered through the trees and left dappled patterns on the forest floor. The air felt crisp and yet soft at the same time, and the sounds of returning life were everywhere. I heard the chirping of birds, the chattering of squirrels—but, of course, what I listened hardest for were the croakings of frogs. I heard a few, but none of them sounded like they had once worked for the government.

Then I heard a thrashing in the underbrush (what little there was of it) right next to the river, and a man came stumbling toward me. It was indeed young Fiske, and my goodness! He fit the definition of *disheveled* so perfectly that all you would have to do is put his picture next to it in the dictionary and folks would get the idea immediately.

"There you are!" I cried. "I've been searching these woods high and low! Everyone has been so worried about you!" (Johnny, that was a little white lie, but I thought it might make him feel better.)

"You have? They have?" he asked wonderingly.

"Yes indeed! I've never heard of anyone setting out to rehabilitate an entire forest all by himself. But not only did you try, you actually succeeded!"

"I—I did? I have?"

"Look around you! Remember what this place was like when you arrived?"

"Well—as I recall, it did look rather dingy."

"That's the understatement of the year!" I assured him. "You know, they once called this place the Dismal Hills. We'll probably have to come up with a new name. You know, I might suggest Fisk's Forest, in honor of you. How does that sound?"

Agent Fisk actually blushed. I didn't think government people could do that. "It would be a great honor, but let's wait a bit. Our policy is not to name places after people until they are dead. The people, that is, not the places."

"I can understand you wanting to wait a bit, in that case," I said.

"But...I can't remember doing anything. I know I came over to give a citation for illegal burning to this really strange old lady, but everything after that seems like kind of a dream."

"I'm not at all surprised. That's a sure sign of overwork, my friend."

"Really?" he said. "I've never experienced it before." (Johnny, for some reason that didn't surprise me a bit.)

"Trust me," I told him. "You've labored so hard over these last four days that you've worn your constitution right down to a frazzle."

"Four days? I've been out here four days?"

"Four days without a letup, working to save this forest. You mean to say you can't recall any of it?" (I was sure hoping that he couldn't.)

"I—I seem to remember that I was squatting down by the riverbank, trying to catch and eat flies." He shook his head in pure wonderment. "And I was *enjoying* it!"

"Hallucination. Brought on by overwork, most likely," I reassured him.

Poor Fiske was so befuddled and bemused that I thought it best to row him back across the river, sit him at my table, fix him a good hot meal and help him write up his report. Yes, you could say I suggested a few things and maybe helped him guild the old lily just a bit. I didn't want more investigators poking around those no-longer-Dismal Hills, you see. Not until I made sure Granny hadn't forgotten anything.

While he was eating and writing and I was serving and suggesting, a fly flew in through an open window and circled around his head. Agent Fiske dropped his pen, stood up, flicked out his tongue, nailed that fly and swallowed it all in one smooth motion. I almost regretted persuading Granny to undo the spell so soon. That young man showed real potential as a frog!

When he realized what he had just done, he gagged and nearly lost his dinner right on the spot. I had to reassure him that it was just another sign of overwork and fatigue, and that a little counseling and a long paid leave would fix him up just fine. I hope he took my advice. He seemed like a nice enough young fellow.

I also hoped that things would return to normal out at Ruination Farm now that Granny had gone back to her proper dimension, and all her unnatural plants and critters had departed with her. It was a relief to believe that.

But it wasn't quite correct.

Old Fluffy

I.

Johnny, the hills across the old Windy River hadn't looked that good in more than a hundred years! The deciduous trees put out new leaves in October. The evergreens turned green again, and I saw flowers, real honest-to-goodness flowers, popping up where only bare, blasted ground had been before. Every day the sun shone on those hills, and every night a gentle rain nurtured them.

Granny Grimoire and her baleful influence were finally gone—that's what the land was telling me. Now a little part of me felt kind of sorry for her. She had tried to do *some* good, after all, and it must be awfully difficult to come from one dimension and then try to operate in another.

I hiked through those woods every day as I listened for the sounds of returning life. The critters were shy in their new environment, and I seldom saw any of them. But I could sense they were making themselves at home, and that made me feel powerful good. Sometimes I wondered about just who or what had stalked those woods while Granny was in residence, but it wasn't a subject I cared to

166

dwell upon. The memories of the skwookuss and the humidaba were still just a little too fresh.

But one fateful morning I was returning from a ramble in those woods when I noticed that the little red flag on my mailbox was up. Now I knew I hadn't put it up, since I had nothing to mail out that day, and it was too early for the RFD man to have brought me anything. So I went over to take a look.

Just as I thought, the box was empty. So I put the flag down and started to walk back to my house. But something made me look back over my shoulder—and lo and otherwise behold! The flag was back up again!

"Great galloping catfish!" I cried out to no one in particular. "Something is amiss and awry here, as sure as the Good Lord made little green avocados!"

I wasn't at all certain I wanted to investigate this peculiar phenomenon. For some reason I could feel a tingle of anxious apprehensions—the kind that could lead to a full-blown case of the blue jimhickies in short order. But I forced myself to march back to the mailbox, open it and take another look inside.

Well, I still didn't see anything. But when I stuck my hand inside and felt around a bit, I discovered an envelope. It was clear at the back and exactly the same color as the box, so it was no wonder I didn't notice it at first. As I drew it out, I wondered just how long it had been there and who had sent it.

"Well, Grandpappy," I said to myself. "There's one quick and easy way to find the answer. Open it up and read it,"

There was no stamp and no writing on the envelope, but inside I found a single scrap of paper with a short message scrawled on it. The handwriting and spelling were both just plain awful, but this was what I finally deciphered.

Dear Grandpappy. Thank you for your friendship and your help. By the time you read this, I will be back in my own dimension again. I have taken almost all my creatures with me, including those snakes you trained to fly. It seemed wrong to leave them behind, and where I come from, snakes are allowed to fly whenever they choose.

But I want you to have a present to remember me by, so I left one little creature behind as a pet for you. I call him Little Fluffy, and I'm sure you will love him. He will probably show up soon after you read this. Farewell and best wishes from your dear friend, Gertrude Grimoire.

My feeling of anxious apprehension quickly turned into a full-blown case of the blue jimhickies as I read that note. Granny had kind of an unnatural sense of humor, and "Little Fluffy" might well turn out to be a 50-foot *tyrannosaurus rex*, for all I knew. But there wasn't much I could do but wait and see what would turn up.

II.

Well, it wasn't a dinosaur, thank goodness for that! The following afternoon, just after I'd finished a hard day's work in the field and was relaxing with a cup of tea and thinking about what I'd fix for supper, I heard a *thump! thump! thump!* at my front door.

"Great galloping catfish!" I cried. "Could that be Little Fluffy?"

I opened the front door, took a look and saw nothing. "Well, if that ain't enough to sour the squash!" I muttered as I went back to my tea.

*Thump! Thump! Thump!*The noise was so loud I dang near dropped the cup. Again I threw open the door and looked around. Not a doggone thing in sight. I started to slam the door again when *Thump!* This time I did drop the cup. The sound came from right at my feet. And when I looked down there, I was too shocked even to cry, "Great galloping catfish!" All I could do was stand there and stare goggle-eyed.

Right at my feet crouched a little green rabbit. That's right, Johnny. A *green* rabbit! And not some washed-out, kinda-sorta green either! This little critter was a bright, bold kelly green—so bright and bold that Kelly, whoever he may have been, would have been proud or envious or maybe both.

"Well now," I said as politely as I could. You must be the little critter Granny left behind for me. Would you like to come in?" Since this was an unnatural critter, it followed that it must have some unnatural abilities. But I didn't know if they included the ability to understand and communicate with humans. However, I thought it best to err on the side of caution and be as polite as possible. Besides, once you got past the color, it did look kinda cute.

The little green rabbit said nothing, but it hopped across the threshold into my house, sat up on its hind legs and had a good look-around—sort of like a prospective tenant deciding if he wanted to move in or not. Meanwhile, I was looking him over like a prospective landlord trying to decide if he would make a good tenant. He did look rather peculiar, after all.

Now this rabbit was not absolutely, totally green. His nose, the lining of his ears and his fluffy little tail were all the color of a ripe pumpkin. I had absolutely no idea as to how old he was, since rabbits are not my specialty and I'd never owned one before. But somehow I got the impression that he was still a youngster and would do some growing if he got the chance.

What did I mean by that last remark? Well, old Hairball, my paranoid cat, was raising violent objections to this rabbit's presence. He stalked around the room all stiff-legged and hissing, with his back arched and his tail bristling out like a bottle brush. I got the immediate impression that these two were not going to get along.

My first instinct was to get little Fluffy out of there before Hairball sliced and diced that strange green rabbit to shreds. The cat was half again the size of little Fluffy. But then I thought, *wait a minute. This little fellow doesn't seem the least bit afraid, and he looks like he knows how to take care of himself. Let's just see what develops here.*

Fluffy didn't move. He just stood his ground and watched that cat with a rather bored expression, as if he were saying, *"Now what's got you so all-fired hot and bothered?"* When Hairball continued to hiss and spit, Fluffy pointed one of his huge ears at him and shook it, almost like an adult shaking a finger at a naughty child. It was as if he was telling that cat to straighten up and mind its manners.

Hairball took a step back and then dropped into a crouch and twitched his tail. I knew he was getting set to pounce, but he never got the chance.

Fluffy lifted one of his big feet—I hadn't noticed until then just how big they were in proportion to the rest of him—and then brought it down good and hard!

WHAM! The jolt lifted Hairball right off the floor. In fact, it nearly knocked me off my feet. The windows rattled, the cupboard doors flew open and another teacup fell to the floor and broke. Little Fluffy was definitely *not* your average rabbit.

At this point Hairball decided that a direct frontal assault was not such a good idea, and that a cessation of hostilities until he could come up with a better plan might be in order. He has some serious emotional problems, but stupidity is not one of them. So he backed off and slunk away. But I had the feeling this was like one of the peace treaties Napoleon would sign just to give him time to regroup and reposition his forces.

Fluffy then hopped over to the front door and looked at it like he wanted to go out. I was glad to oblige, but I noticed that when he hopped, his feet were no louder then those of your average bunny. That goshawful stomp must be a kind of defense mechanism that he only used when he had to.

At least I *hoped* that was the only time he made use of that particular talent. My house dates from clear back before the turn of the century (and I can't say for sure which century), and it wouldn't take very many of those terrible stomps to bring the whole place right down around my ears. It looked like I might have a one-rabbit demolition company on my hands, and there was no way I could track Granny down and return her farewell present, since she was apparently back in another dimension now.

So it looked like I was stuck with Fluffy. But what was I going to do with him?

III.

You see, Johnny, I was sure that little green rabbit had some kind of talent that I might put to good use. He reminded me a little of the popapple Granny gave me. The apple itself was horrible, but the pips were what counted. There had to be a blessing in that bunny somewhere. Of course, being one of Granny's gifts, it was probably a mixed blessing. Probably very mixed indeed!

So I observed that little critter closely as he hopped around the farm. He seemed completely unafraid of all the farm animals. I guess he sensed that none of them would do him any harm. I wondered how he knew that, since he had little or no experience with beings of this world. Then I began to notice his ears.

I told you they were big and they were, even for a rabbit. But they weren't what you would call outlandishly large. No, it was what Fluffy was doing with them that caused me to pause and shake my head in wonderment.

He would hop a few paces and then let one ear go limp until it actually trailed on the ground. But the other remained stiff as an ax handle, and he kept it pointed straight up at the sky, no matter what the position of his head. And Johnny, I do believe that ear seemed to be swiveling! That little critter was up to something, all right. But what?

Then all of a sudden that bunny sat up, full alert, and pointed *both* ears straight up at the sky for a second or so. Then he wheeled and sprinted back to the house as fast as he could, not stopping until he was crouched right beside me on the porch.

Obviously, something had spooked him, but what could it be? I looked all around and couldn't see anything out of the ordinary. Then I noticed both his ears were still pointed straight up at the sky and swiveling slightly, as though they were following the flight of something. So I got clear down on my stomach, sighted along the line where his ears were pointing, and I saw what had spooked him.

It was a big old red-tail hawk soaring in a lazy circle above the farm. It must have been close to a thousand feet above the earth, and I never would have spotted it unless I had known just where to look. That little bunny must have picked it out with just a glance up into the sky!

"How did you do that, Little Fluffy?" I asked it. "Why, you must have a set of eyeballs as good as that hawk's! Maybe even better!"

And do you know that little rabbit must have understood me? It just gave me a little grin and shook its head as if to say, "Nope. That's not how I did it."

"Well," I said as I squatted down beside him, "if you didn't see it, then how in blazes did you know it was up there?"

Then, as if to answer me, that bunny waggled both his ears and then swiveled each one in a full circle. Then he let one droop while the other pointed straight up into the sky. I took a sighting along it and there was that red-tail, still circling over Ruination Farm!

"Do you mean to tell me you can hear the air passing over that hawk's wings when it's close to a thousand feet above us?" I asked even more wonderingly than before.

Fluffy just nodded as if to say, "What's so peculiar about that?"

"Well, If that isn't enough to grease the gooseberries!" I muttered. That little green bunny had himself a special talent, sure enough! The question that remained for me was just how was I going to put it to use?

IV.

I turned that question over and over in my mind during the next few weeks, but the answer always seemed to stay just out of reach. "Now if this isn't a predicament powerful enough to pulverize the potatoes!" I said right out loud to myself. "Just how am I going to use this little green critter's talent to enrich mankind—and myself?" (For you see, Johnny, I was never one to turn down a few extra dollars.) Well, like a lot of humankind's great discoveries, the answer came quite by accident.

It happened a couple of months later, just before Christmas. The snow hadn't come yet, but a week of steady rain had kept us all of us pretty much cooped up in the house. I didn't mind it so much, since the crops were in and I had a stack of good books I could plow through. But I'm afraid that Hairball and Fluffy weren't readers, and time was beginning to weigh kind of heavily on them.

By this time Fluffy had grown to where he was now half again as big as Hairball, so I was pretty sure that cat had given up all thought of messing with him. Not that they had become good buddies— not by a long shot! Each kept to his own side of the room and pretended that the other wasn't there. I even had to fix separate litter boxes.

Then the bad weather broke and the sun came out again. Hairball and Fluffy both demanded to go out, and I figured it was a good idea. By this time Fluffy was big enough to be safe on his own, and Hairball was an old hand at roaming and prowling. Each made it plain that he would go his own separate way, but I had no misgivings about turning them loose.

But maybe I should have.

Fluffy came back around sundown, but there was no sign of old Hairball. This didn't worry me much, since cats like to prowl at night. When there was no sign of him next morning, though, I began to get a little concerned. You see, I'd set out a bowl of his favorite Kitty Treats, and Hairball is not a cat to let a treat go unsampled. By noon my concern was turning into a case of the blue jimhickies.

That cat was in trouble—I could sense it! But where was he?

Now if this were a scene from a movie or a book, I'd just tell Ol' Blue, my faithful hunting dog, to find the missing critter, and the two of us would go running off to the rescue. But I didn't have a dog named Blue—or Green—or any other color you might think of. I didn't have any dog at all—just that worthless, paranoid cat and the unnatural rabbit.

And, you might wonder, why was there no dog around the place? Well, I don't go hunting any more, since the joy of killing things no longer appeals to me. Plus, you have to care for a dog, but a cat will care for itself. Just put out a little food once in a while, change the litter every now and then, give it a warm spot by the fire to sleep, and you've got yourself a companion for life. It's not always that affectionate, and it won't lick your face and slobber on you, but it's there.

But just then old Hairball *wasn't* there, and what was I going to do? If there was such a place as Hertz Rent-a-Hound, I would have called them up and placed an order. But I knew I would have to make do with what was on the premises. How could I go about it?

Then I became aware of that little green rabbit standing there at my feet.

"Oh Fluffy!" I said sadly. "If only you could track like a dog, I would sure put you to work right now!"

Fluffy just looked at me, nodded his little green head and hopped outside like he was bent on doing just that. I was more than a bit doubtful, since rabbits are not really known for their sense of smell. But was I ever due for the surprise of my life!

As soon as we were well clear of the house, Fluffy gave me a look as if warning me to brace myself. Then he lifted his enormous right foot and brought it down good and hard.

WHAM! To say the ground shook was an understatement. Braced as I was, it nearly jolted me right off my feet. Yes, that ground actually shook, just like we were having an earthquake! Magnitude 6 on the old Richter Scale, at least. All my critters started carrying on like the end of the world was at hand, and I knew my hens would lay pre-scrambled eggs for at least a week. Just what was that unnatural rabbit up to?

Fluffy paid no heed to the consternation and commotion he had caused. He stood bolt upright with both ears swiveling in complete circles. Suddenly one of them stopped and pointed east by southeast. Then the other pointed the same way. They seemed to be locked in on something—but what?

Well, Johnny, that rabbit began running in the direction his ears pointed, and just like before, his feet made almost no sound as he passed over the ground. He covered about two hundred yards. Then he stopped, shot me that same warning look and raised his right foot once again.

WHAM! This time I was better prepared, and it didn't take me quite so long to recover my balance. Once more Fluffy's ears swiveled, locked in on something I sure couldn't hear, and away he hopped again. But I noticed he'd altered course by a few degrees and was now bearing more to the south.

This went on for a good ten minutes and another five or six earth-shaking stomps. Fluffy ran in kind of a zig-zag pattern, but always in the same general direction. I found myself deep in the throes of a peculiar puzzlement. Doggone if that kelly green rabbit didn't remind me a bit of a hound dog following a cold scent.

Then it hit me. That was exactly what that bunny was doing!

That unnatural rabbit was following a cold sound!

Let me try to explain what I mean by that. Just about any living critter will leave a scent behind him wherever he goes. You and I can't smell it, but a good hound dog can, and he can follow a scent trail as easily as you or I can follow footprints. Eventually, of course, the scent settles into the ground and grows fainter and fainter until it's too far gone for even the best bloodhound to pick up.

But, Johnny, here's the point. *Does it ever disappear completely?* Would a dog with an infinitely powerful smeller be able to pick it up weeks, months or maybe even years later? Well, I'll let the philosophers speculate on that one.

But do you recall another question those philosopher folks like to pose—the one about a tree falling in the forest and nobody hearing it, so does it make a sound? Well, I'll tell you what it does do. *It creates sound waves!* And would it be possible to backtrack a sound wave the same way a hound dog might follow a cold scent? Yes, I know you or I couldn't. But what about a critter like Fluffy? Would it be possible for him? Well, just then I was hoping and praying that it was, because that looked like the only chance we had of finding poor Hairball.

That unnatural rabbit's actions seemed perfectly natural all of a sudden. Fluffy was pounding the ground just like my great-aunt Hester used to beat the carpets every spring, I remember how the dust would fly every time she whacked them. Well, Fluffy was doing the same thing to dear old Mother Earth. Why, I could almost see those long-gone sound waves spring back to life and take to the air again every time his foot came down!

As soon as I realized what he was doing, I backed off and followed at some distance as quietly as I could. After all, I didn't want to make any additional sounds that might distract him. But Fluffy was so caught up in his work that I doubt if he would have noticed an elephant stampede—unless of course they cut across the sound he was following.

V.

We had trailed old Hairball's footfalls about three-quarters of the way across the far meadow when Fluffy suddenly stopped, leaned forward and pointed both ears at a spot just a few feet ahead. Dang if he didn't remind me of a bird dog going on point! I looked where he was pointing and saw the ground was all messed up, like a considerable battle had taken place there recently. I also found a few drops of what appeared to be blood. Things weren't looking very good for old Hairball.

Then, a few feet farther on, I saw another patch of mussed-up ground and some more blood. I also found some feathers, which I knew from experience (since I once taught night-school classes in ornithology at one of our major universities) came from one of the *accipiter* family.

(All right, Johnny. I won't make you look that one up. Raptors. Hawks. That's what they are. As to just what kind—well, a cooper's hawk wouldn't be big enough, and an osprey is only interested in fish. Of course, a big old eagle would have nailed Hairball cleanly. No, this one was just about big enough to carry off that cat, but maybe not quite. My guess would be a goshawk or maybe a redtail.)

Whatever it was, it appeared that old Hairball had put up quite a fight. I was willing to bet that not all the blood at the scene of the battle was his, and I was beginning to hope that maybe, just *maybe*, he'd been able to fight his way clear and make his escape. But if that was the case, then where was he now?

"Fluffy," I said, "Hairball is about the most worthless cat in all creation, but I've developed a real affection for the paranoid old so-and-so. So if you can find him in time, I'll be more than grateful."

Fluffy nodded as if he understood and gave the ground another goshawful stomp. I could almost swear I saw the sound waves float up into the air just like the dust my great-aunt raised when she beat the carpets.

The trail was getting warmer—or maybe louder, although I still couldn't hear anything. Hairball or what was left of him must be close by, but could we find him in time? I found myself talking, half to myself and half to Fluffy, urging him on and giving encouragement he probably didn't need.

"C'mon, Fluffy Old Fellow! Find that cat for me! Keep to the scent—er, the sound, that is! I know you can do it!" See, critters may not be able to understand every word you say to them, but they can pick up the general idea. That rabbit understood my concern, if not my words, and that's what spurred him on.

Fluffy followed the trail to a small grove of trees at the far end of the meadow. The cat had apparently sought cover, which made sense. But Fluffy ran into trouble once we reached the trees. Trailing by sound must be a lot more difficult in close quarters like a small forest. I guess the sound waves must bounce and echo off the trunks or get tangled up in the undergrowth. It was probably worse than following the scent of a crafty old fox or raccoon who would double back and cross his own trail again.

But we had to be close. That cat couldn't have dragged himself all that far after what he'd been through. I began to whistle and call his name. Fluffy must have sensed what I was doing because he stopped stomping the ground and began swiveling his ears like radar scanners. Suddenly they stopped and seemed to lock in on something. I carefully moved forward about a dozen paces. Then I heard it too.

"Meow!"

It was the cry of a cat in considerable trouble and pain. I dropped to my knees, groped through the underbrush and finally found poor Hairball cowering under some ferns. He looked mighty torn up, but nothing appeared to be broken.

I lifted him out as carefully as I could and examined his wounds. He'd managed to lick some of them clean, but he couldn't reach those on his back and neck, and they were already beginning to fester. Add in the fact that a couple of them looked pretty deep, and you can understand why I felt another case of the blue jimhickies coming on.

"Well now, Old Hairball," I said as we started back for the house, "it appears you are due for a date with the vet—and let's hope he is also a first-class seamstress!" I was trying to make light of it so as not to scare him. But that cat must have sensed the concern in my voice, because for once he raised no objection to a visit to the vet.

"You'd best wait here," I told Fluffy as I carefully loaded the cat in my truck. "I don't know if the town is ready just yet for a bright green rabbit who makes the ground shake when he stomps a foot." Actually, Johnny, I was afraid some agency would grab him for study and I'd never see him again. Besides, if old By-and-By Jones, the now-reformed town drunk, saw Fluffy in all his green glory, he might go right back on the sauce.

VI.

The vet insisted on keeping Hairball a couple of days "for observation" (and to pad his bill, no doubt). So I drove back to Ruination Farm empty-handed. Fluffy met me right as I parked, and he looked as concerned as a bright green bunny could look.

"He's going to be all right, Fluffy Old Fellow," I reassured him. "I'll fetch him back from the vet day after tomorrow." And dang if old Fluffy didn't nod his head just like he understood every word I'd just said.

Two days later, as I drove back to town to pick up the cat, I began ruminating on just how I could communicate with old Fluffy. I could swear that he knew what I said when I spoke to him. But I wanted to know what was on his mind as well, and rabbits, even bright green rabbits, are not known for their vocal skills. Just how could I open a two-way communication with him? There had to be an answer somewhere.

Well, the answer came in two parts. First off, I had just parked the truck and was walking over to the Snodgrass County Veterinary Hospital and Animal Correctional Facility when I saw Si Perkins communicating up a storm with his cousin Zeb. You see, Zeb is as deaf as the statue of General Snodgrass out on the courthouse lawn, but both he and Si were fluent in American Sign Language. They chattered away like mad as they strolled down the street, and nobody heard a word they said.

That was part one of my solution, but it wouldn't do all by itself. True, Fluffy seemed intelligent enough to learn signing, but I doubted if his little front paws could handle the complexities of the English language. Then, as I passed the flagpole by the post office and saw Old Glory flapping in the breeze, the second part of the solution smacked me like a slap to the face.

Semaphore, Johnny! Signal flags! That was it!

You don't see semaphore flags around anymore. But back in the days of the Civil War (and no, I'm not *that* old), they used them to send signals across the battlefield. You held a signal flag in each hand and moved them up, down or across in various combinations that spelled out what you wanted to say.

I didn't expect old Fluffy to hold flags, but he could move his ears just like a semaphore signaler. If I could teach him a code that we both understood, then I could communicate with him directly and know just exactly what was on his mind. Was such a thing possible? Well, it was sure worth a try.

That very night, while poor Hairball lay recuper-
ating in his bed, I started teaching Fluffy his ABC's.
He was an unnaturally smart rabbit (which was only
natural, since he was an unnatural rabbit to begin
with) and caught on to the general idea in almost no
time. Why, after just one lesson we could communicate on a simple, basic level.

"Hungry dinner want," he signaled with
those huge ears of his. The sequence was a little
off, but the meaning was plain enough. Later it was,
"Bed fire sleep," and I assumed he was asking me to
make up his bed close to the fire, since it was a chilly
evening. Of course, being an unnatural rabbit, he
might have been asking to sleep in the fire itself. But
I would have been opposed to that.

Next morning, as soon as I was up and fixing my
tea, Fluffy signaled, "Carrot two outside," meaning
(I assumed) that he would like to take his breakfast
of two carrots out on the front porch. As I handed
them over and opened the front door for him, he
signaled, "Better cat good." I took that to mean he
was glad old Hairball was feeling a bit better—or it
could mean it would be good if we got a better cat. I
could see where syntax might be a problem in our
communication.

But, Johnny, we *could* communicate! That was
the spice in the old cider. I now had a rabbit with a
perfectly unique tracking system, plus the ability to
let me know what was on his mind. The potential
uses for his talents seemed endless, if I could just
find a way to cash in on them. But the chance would
come up. I was sure of that.

VII.

Well, the opportunity came up just a few weeks later and, wonder of wonders, it was my ordinary neighbors to the north, the Finsters, who provided it. Think of it, Johnny! The Finsters! A family so normal that *Ordinary People* magazine had just named them one of the Ten Most Ordinary Families in America!

I had heard they were being considered for this honor—if you can call it that—and I'd stayed away from them while they were being checked out. After all, I'm just a little out of the ordinary myself, and I didn't want to ruin their chance at seeing themselves in the pages of their favorite magazine.

I figured to go pay them a call and congratulate them after the excitement at being chosen had worn off and they'd had a chance to get back to being their normal, ordinary selves again. But fate, it seems, had other ideas, and the Finster family's lives were about to take a very sudden, unexpected and—yes—dramatic turn.

Now, Johnny, take a moment to try to comprehend just how unlikely all this was. This was a family that ate, slept, lived and breathed ordinariness. For them even to think of doing something out of the ordinary was about as unlikely as old Hairball actually making himself useful.

But just before noon on an otherwise normal and uneventful Monday morning, I began getting phone calls. The first was from Fred Finster's place of employment. He worked as a quality control foreman at Flynn's Fabulous Fudge Factory (which is

Snodgrass County's largest single employer). Fred Finster had not shown up for work as he always did at precisely 7:55 each morning. Furthermore, Fred Finster was not answering his phone. Since I was their nearest neighbor, could I please check into it?

Very curious and unforseen, I thought as I put down the phone. Was something amiss and awry with the Finsters? It hardly seemed possible.

But my hand had scarcely left the receiver when the phone rang again. This time it was Phillip Phillmore Elementary School over in Elsewhere, where Fred's wife Frances taught fourth grade. She had not shown up for work. Neither had she called in with any explanation. Could I please check that out?

I had just made up my mind to go over to the Finster family home to see if anything was wrong—in fact, I was just reaching for my coat—when the phone rang a third time. It was the school the two Finster children attended. They were both absent, and Frankie Finster had a soccer match that afternoon, while his sister Felicia was due to give a flute recital. Nobody answered the phone at the Finster family residence, so would I please see if anything was wrong?

Now I was growing worried. Frankie Finster was a very dutiful if ordinary player who would never let his team down by failing to show up. Felicia was good with the flute—good in an ordinary sort of way, of course—and would never miss a performance in the normal course of events. So something quite abnormal must be fulminating in the Finster Family. Very curious indeed!

Maybe I might need some help, I thought as I headed out to my truck. Of course, anything having to do with help automatically eliminated old Hairball, but Fluffy might be able to assist me. So I whistled for that bunny and explained in word and sign that his services might be needed.

"Help glad you give," he signaled back, which I took to mean he was willing. So I told Hairball we'd be back in a short while, loaded Fluffy into the truck and drove on over to the Finster place.

The Finsters' ordinary house was set at the end of an ordinary drive, but when I started to turn in, Fluffy signaled for me to stop. I guess he sensed something was wrong, so I let him out to investigate.

Fluffy hopped a dozen or so yards up the driveway. Then he paused, raised his right foot and brought it down with a goshawful *whomp!* Immediately both ears swiveled and then locked in on the driveway.

"Car go yesterday out, back come not," he signaled.

I got out and walked up the driveway after him. Sure enough, the Finster family's familiar four-year-old Ford station wagon was missing. *"Mysteriouser and mysteriouser!"* I said as I knocked on the door and got no answer. "Fred? Frances? Frankie? Felicia?" I called out, but there was no response.

I tried the door and found it was unlocked. (Yes, it's true. Crime is almost unheard of in these parts, so people actually leave their doors unlocked most of the time.) I walked through the house calling their names, but all I got for my trouble was a spooky

silence. There were no signs of a commotion or
struggle, and nothing seemed to be missing—nothing except the four Finsters, that is.

"Fluffy!" I called out as I left the house. "Can
you tell how many Finsters got into that Ford?"

Again Fluffy went *whomp!* Then he signaled,
"Four big two small two."

So all four Finsters were in the familiar family
Ford. But just where was that familiar family Ford?
I was developing a bad case of the blue jimhickies.
Something extraordinary had apparently happened
to one of the nation's ten most ordinary families, and
I had some real reservations about the Finsters' abil-
ity to deal with the extraordinary. But at least I now
knew what I had to do.

"Fluffy," I said to that unnatural green rabbit, "we
have to find the Finsters' Ford, because that's
probably where they are. And I have a notion that
we need to do it pronto and quick, as in the sooner
the better!"

VIII.

Since yesterday had been Sunday, I figured the
Finsters had gone for their customary Sunday drive,
just like they did every week. But now it was Monday and they hadn't returned. Where could they
be? Well, I thanked my lucky stars, the Good Lord
and Granny Grimoire (not necessarily in that order)
that I had a fine tracking rabbit!

Fluffy hopped back to the end of the ordinary
driveway. Then he stopped, stomped and swiveled
his ears and started back up the road, heading north

towards and then past Ruination Farm. I followed at a distance in the truck.

Luckily there was no traffic on the Old Stage Road that morning, since I was afraid an oncoming car might confuse the sound pattern—to say nothing of what effect a very large green rabbit might have on the oncoming driver. We had just passed Milepost 28 (where, as you might recall, I had delivered that herd of catfish to Myer O'Dwyer), when we came to a fork in the road and Fluffy hesitated.

Johnny, I was starting to develop a case of the queasy uneasies on top of the blue jimhickies that I already had. You see, if you took the right fork, you stayed on the Old Stage Road and eventually it took you to Somewhere. But the left fork was an even older section of the road, and it wound along the old Windy River right up past Parker's Knot. That was one treacherous piece of highway, which was why it had been pretty much abandoned years ago. I don't think anyone lived along it.

Could the Finsters, flushed with their success, have gotten just a bit daring and decided to take an unfamiliar road on their Sunday drive? Sure enough, Fluffy's ears swiveled left and he began to hop down what must have been the oldest and most deserted stretch of road in all of Snodgrass County.

Any road that seeks to parallel the Windy River has to do close to thirty miles of loops and twists to cover what would be three miles in a straight line, which is why nobody in his right mind ever tries to drive it. I don't even think people in their wrong minds would make the attempt unless they absolutely had to.

But apparently the Finsters, whose lives were the epitome of everyday experiences, had attempted just that. "Find those Finster folk, Fluffy!" I yelled after the rabbit as he hopped down the road. Then I jumped back in the truck and gunned the engine, because I had a powerful premonition that there was trouble up ahead!

Fluffy actually stayed ahead of me, even though I floorboarded my old truck and took those hairpin curves with two wheels on the ground and two more spinning in the air. You see, that unnatural bunny could cut across the loops and save maybe nine-tenths the distance I had to drive. So even going flat-out, I had a hard time keeping him in sight.

Slow it down, Grandpappy! I cautioned myself as I tore through one of those hairpin loops far faster than I should. *You're not driving at Le Mans anymore!* (Yes, Johnny, I did drive in that famous race—though modesty compels me to add that it was only once and I finished back toward the middle of the pack.) I was just easing back a bit when I saw old Fluffy up ahead signaling with his ears for me to stop.

I immediately hit the brakes, pulled up beside him and asked, "What news, Old Fluffy? Have you found something?"

"Car road off ahead inside trap people," he signaled back. I took that to mean that a car had run off the road somewhere up ahead, and there were people trapped inside it.

"Great galloping catfish, Fluffy! Are they in the river?" The old Windy was mighty deep and treacherous along this particular stretch.

"Close no but very. Caution approach with must." I was going to have to work with that rabbit on his sentence structure, but this was hardly the time. I got out of the truck and followed him on foot, noticing as I did that he hopped very cautiously and no longer paused to stomp the ground. Whatever happened must have happened close by, but dang if I could see anything suspicious or suggestive.

Then he stopped with his ears pointing off to the left. This particular stretch of the Even Older Stage Road had a thick belt of trees and undergrowth that spread from the shoulder of the road right down to the riverbank itself. As I looked where old Fluffy pointed, I saw a hole in the brush. Something had gone crashing through it very recently.

"Great galloping catfish!" I exclaimed again. "Fluffy! What happened here?"

"Bang tire go car road off," that unnaturally green bunny signaled back.

As we approached, I caught the glint of metal in the foliage. Then I saw the Finster Family Ford stuck between two trees. Not stuck very tightly though. Those two trees must have been just enough to stop the Finsters at the last possible instant. I could tell because the Ford's front tires were resting on nothing but air over a drop of a good twenty feet right into the old Windy! I signaled Fluffy to stay back and then crept a little closer. I could see four very frightened Finster faces peering at me through the back window.

That back window opens, I thought. *Why don't they just crawl out?* Then I took a closer look and realized the answer.

You see, by rights the Finsters should have wound up in the river, but those trees had stopped them at the last possible instant. But that station wagon was balanced on the edge just like a teeter-totter, and it was only the combined weight of the four Finsters crowded in the back that kept it in place. If they opened the window, one of the four might make it out, but the effect of his or her escape would be exactly the same as a child jumping off the end of an evenly-balanced teeter-totter. That Ford and the remaining Finsters would go right straight down into the old Windy, and I wouldn't give very good odds on any more of them making it out!

Fortunately, Johnny, I believe in being prepared for any emergencies that might come up. I warned the Finsters to stay put, not to move a muscle, and I would be right back with just what was needed. Then I ran back to my truck and pulled out a length of old logging chain and a couple of clamps. You never know when things like that are going to come in mighty handy.

It was also fortunate that I used to set chokers back in my younger days in the lumber camps of Oregon and Washington. Thus I knew exactly what to do with the Finster Family Ford. I set one end of the chain around the rear axle, secured it with a clamp, ran back to a good-sized hemlock, took two turns around its trunk with the other end and clamped it good and tight.

"Okay, you Finster Folk," I said as casually as I could—for they still weren't out of the woods (or rather the car) yet. "It's time to make a careful exit. Let's have Felicia come out first."

Fred Finster already had the window rolled down, and he carefully handed his daughter out to me. The result was just as I had calculated. No sooner had little Felicia's weight left the back end than the Finster Family Ford lurched forward on what would have been its final, fatal plunge into the old Windy. But my chain held it! One by one the Finsters climbed out, until they were all standing on good old *terra firma* once again.

I put all four Finsters in the back of my truck, drove them back to their ordinary house at the end of that ordinary driveway and dropped them off— telling them I'd be back after they'd had a chance to collect and compose themselves. Why did the whole family choose to ride back in the bed of my truck, in open defiance of our state motor vehicle code? Remember, Johnny, they'd gone at least twenty-four hours without food or water—or bathroom facilities. Add the state of mortal terror they had all been in and you can see why they didn't want to get back in another enclosed compartment right away.

Can't say as I blame them.

IX.

Fluffy did not ride back with us. He had hopped back on his own and, by cutting across the loops in the Even Older Stage Road, had managed to keep ahead of us and hence out of sight. I figured he would head straight for Ruination Farm, and I couldn't be sure if the Finsters had caught sight of him or not. It was then that I found myself in the throes of a querulous quandary. *Did I want the Finsters to know about Fluffy or not?*

After all, Fluffy had been the one to find them, and I shouldn't take the credit when he had done most of the work. But on the other hand, the Finsters were officially one of the ten most ordinary families in America, and they had just been through the most terrifying ordeal in their otherwise ordinary lives. Would it be right to tell them they had been rescued by an unnatural green rabbit who had tracked them down by sound?

Well, I finally decided it was Fluffy's decision and he should therefore be the one to make the call. So I drove back to Ruination Farm and put the question to him. He thought it over a bit and then signaled that yes, he would be willing to meet the family.

So I loaded him in the truck with me and off we went to face the Finsters. I was expecting a greeting that would be a little warmer then usual, but I sure wasn't prepared for what I got! Fred Finster grabbed me in a bear hug as soon as he opened the door. Frances gave me a big kiss on the cheek, then set me on their sofa, where Frankie and Felicia hopped on my lap and repeated the process.

"Listen up, you friendly Finsters!" I said as soon as I could untangle myself. "I want you all to meet Fluffy. He's the one who found you. I just followed him along."

Johnny, I wasn't sure how this was going to go down. To take one of America's Ten Most Ordinary Families, put them through a world-class trauma, and then tell them they owed their lives to a large green rabbit from another dimension—would they be able to accept such a thing?

Oh my, did they ever! Frankie and Felicia immediately turned loose of me and grabbed on to Fluffy—for which I was grateful. They took turns holding, petting and hugging him, and it appeared that green bunny enjoyed every second of it. I don't think there's all that much affection in Granny's dimension, and I must admit I don't hold and cuddle animals as much as I used to.

"Well," I observed, "I'm glad to see you've all apparently recovered from your ordeal. Is everyone all right? No immediate signs of post-traumatic this-or-that? Do you think you can get back to being your ordinary selves again?"

"No!" Fred answered me. "We are not all right, and we don't ever plan to be!"

"Come again?" I asked. This was very un-Finsterlike.

"We all got to talking things over while we were waiting to see if we would live or die," Frances Finster explained to me. "I'm afraid we came to the conclusion that our lives had been so ordinary and predictable that they were, well, *boring.*

"Exactly!" Fred agreed, and Frankie and Felicia nodded as well. "We decided that if by some miracle we were spared, we would devote the rest of our days to becoming the most *unusual* family on the face of the earth!"

"Do tell!" was all I could say.

"We mean it!" Fred assured me. "I have just called Flynn's Fabulous Fudge Factory to announce my resignation as their quality control foreman." He then gave me the biggest smile I had seen on a human face in years. "I've always had this dream of being a secret agent! Tomorrow I'm applying for a job with the CIA!"

"Uh, Fred. Isn't that a bit of a jump? I mean, going from fudge to secret intelligence in one leap?"

"Not at all, Grandpappy. Quality control is quality control, no matter where you work. You simply have to make sure the ingredients are correct and properly mixed and the finished product is easily digestible. Isn't that so?"

I could see where Fred Finster might have a future in intelligence. "What about you, Frances?" I asked his wife.

"I'm resigning my teaching position as soon as the school can find a replacement," she announced. "Snodgrass County children are very nice, but they're all so predictable. I've always dreamed of running a gourmet restaurant specializing in the cuisine of Nepal and Tibet. So now I'm going to do it! Won't that be wonderful?"

"You may not find that many customers here in Snodgrass County," I noted. "We're mostly meat-and-potatoes folk around these parts."

"I know," she replied. "We're all going to be moving soon. This county is nice, but it's all so *ordinary* here! And we want to give the children the opportunity to expand their horizons."

"Really? Which way do you think your horizons will expand?" I asked Frankie, who at twelve was the older of the two Finster kids.

"Well, Grandpappy, I'm getting just a bit tired of Little League and soccer camps, but there is one sport I'd really like to try."

"And what is that?" I asked. I wasn't all that surprised Frankie would choose a sport, since he was athletic in an ordinary sort of way.

"The pentathlon! Do you know what it is, Grandpappy? It's in the Olympics, you know."

"Yes, I'm familiar with it, Frankie. No American has ever won it."

"That's going to change when I get to the Olympics!" Frankie replied.

Johnny, that lad's voice had a note of steel and determination I had never heard from a Finster before. The modern pentathlon is five tough events: running, swimming, fencing, pistol shooting and horseback riding. I know because I was on the U.S. National Team myself, back in my younger days— though modesty compels me to add that I was only the first alternate and never got a chance to compete at the Olympic level.

"And what about you?" I asked Felicia, who was ten. "I hope you're not going to give up your music. I think you have some real talent there." (She really did show some ordinary promise on her flute.)

"I'm staying with my music, but I'm switching from the flute to the contrabassoon," she informed me. "There has never been a real contrabassoon virtuoso in the history of music. I'm going to be the first."

Johnny, she sounded just as determined as her brother. Of course her choice of instrument surprised me just a bit, since a contrabassoon is bigger than she was. Felicia Finster was a petite little thing, and her size had helped win the family their spot on the Ten Most Ordinary list. See, the ordinary family was supposed to have 1.91 kids, and Felicia was exactly 91% of the normal size for a child her age. That's great for statistical averages, not so great for the contrabassoon.

"Felicia, Honey, I don't believe there's been very much written for that particular instrument," I said.

"I know," she said. "I'll compose it." And the determination in her voice told me that she would.

"You see, Grandpappy," her brother chimed in, "the pentathlon and the contrabassoon are secondary careers. We're both going into veterinary medicine."

"That's right," Felicia added. "We want to specialize in the care of rare and exotic animals." She looked longingly at Fluffy and added, "Just like that wonderful green bunny you have, Grandpappy!"

X.

Johnny, her last comment came as a solution to a ponderous problem that was pestering and perplexing me on the drive over to the Finsters. *What should Fluffy's future be?*

Should I keep that unnatural green rabbit with me at Ruination Farm? Would he be happy with just me and old Hairball for company? What would happen when the world at large found out about him and his unique abilities? I could close my eyes and picture official government officials arriving by the carload. I could see him being officially requisitioned or maybe even bunnynapped.

On he other hand, what would happen if I gave him to the Finsters? Well, I might miss out on my chance for fame and fortune as the owner of the world's most unusual and talented rabbit. But, Johnny, I've had my fill of fame and fortune, and I really don't need any more of it. And who knows? Fluffy might be able to help the Finsters achieve their highly improbable goals—or at least a portion of them.

What clinched it was something Fred Finster had told me the previous week. The family owned a dog, of course. This particular fido was a very ordinary mutt of no special breed, a generous nature and one bad habit. It liked to chase cars. Unfortunately, this bowser had pursued one minivan too many and bought himself a one-way ticket to that great dog-house in the sky. The Finsters were still mourning their loss when they made the top ten list. Maybe Fluffy would be just what they needed.

But of course it wouldn't be fair to make the offer without first consulting Fluffy and finding out his thoughts on the subject. So I asked the Finsters to excuse us for a moment, took Fluffy outside and put the question to him.

"Fluffy," I said. "Would you like to come back to Ruination Farm with me or remain here with the Finsters and be their pet?"

Fluffy swiveled his ears for several seconds and then signaled back, "Grandpappy much you like very but more Finsters me need." It took me a second or so to unscramble the sentence, but once I got the meaning, I knew old Fluffy was right.

"Then let's go tell them," I said, and we did.

The Finsters were in fine fettle indeed when I presented them with Fluffy. I showed them how he signaled with his ears and promised to send over a manual so they could decipher what he had to say. Then we all went outside and I had Fluffy stomp for them. They all agreed it was a marvelous talent. In fact, little Felicia, who had the sharpest ears (Remember, she was the musician of the family.), said that she could actually hear a few of the sounds that Fluffy brought up.

It was kind of lonely driving back to Ruination Farm all by myself. But it looked like Fluffy would have a really good home with the Finsters, and I would finally be able to enjoy a little peace and quiet for a change. I wondered just how long the Finsters would be able to keep Fluffy a secret from the world at large—but hey, that was their problem now. Fluffy had saved their lives. What they did with the rest of their days was now up to them.

Old Hairball let on that he was mighty lonesome for that unnatural green rabbit, but I knew it was all for show. I told him that Fluffy's new home was less than a mile away and that he could go visit him any time, but Hairball made no effort to do so. As winter began to close in on Ruination Farm once again, he curled up on his favorite rug next to the hearth and began the process of snoozing away the days.

XI.

Johnny, I'm glad to hear you're coming for a visit soon, but I'm afraid you'll find Ruination Farm a little dull after all is said and done. Arnold Bennett and his surviving squadron mates are off flying in some other dimension—and I'm afraid the last of my popapple pips went down the greedy gullet of that obsnifferous old scaleywag of a humidaba.

Add in the fact that the Finsters are moving to parts unknown next week and taking old Fluffy with them, and that the last of the great galloping catfish went extinct when poor old Sil drowned, and that Granny took Hippo with her when she left—well, there might not be much to see and do around these parts.

But then again, maybe there will be. Strange things have been known to happen out at Ruination Farm.

The End*

*Or is it? With Grandpappy, you never can be sure.